Values of $(1/e)^{\overline{X}}$

$\overline{X}$	$(1/e)^{\overline{X}}$	$\overline{X}$	$(1/e)^{\overline{X}}$	$\overline{X}$	$(1/e)^{\overline{X}}$
.01	.990	0.1	.905	1.0	.368
.02	.980	0.2	.819	2.0	.135
.03	.970	0.3	.741	3.0	.0498
.04	.961	0.4	.670	4.0	.0183
.05	.951	0.5	.607	5.0	.00674
.06	.942	0.6	.549	6.0	.00248
.07	.932	0.7	.497	7.0	.00091
.08	.923	0.8	.449	8.0	.00034
.09	.914	0.9	.407	9.0	.00012

Use of the Table in Poisson Probability

If an event is of the sort that can happen at any instant (like a traffic accident or the decay of an atom) and either theory or past experience indicates that $\overline{X}$ occurrences are to be expected in a certain period of time, then the probability that no occurrences will take place in that time equals $(1/e)^{\overline{X}}$ and the probability for exactly X occurrences is

$$P\left\{x\right\} = \frac{\overline{X}}{X}\, P\left\{x-1\right\}.$$

THE
WORLD
OF
PROBABILITY

THE
WORLD
OF
PROBABILITY

Statistics in Science

BY

SOLOMON DIAMOND

Basic Books, Inc., Publishers

NEW YORK · LONDON

I am indebted to the late Sir Ronald A. Fisher, F.R.S., Cambridge, and to Messrs. Oliver & Boyd, Ltd., Edinburgh, publishers, for permission to reprint tables III and 11 from their book, *Statistical Methods for Research Workers,* and permission to quote a passage from their book, *The Design of Experiment.*

Introduction

THIS THING
ABOUT NUMBERS

●

STATISTICS involve numbers. There are no numbers in nature, only things and processes. Numbers are an invention, a tool of human mastery over nature. It is not surprising, therefore, that the use of numbers is not natural, just as a good golf stroke is not natural and a good swimming style is not natural. These are cultivated skills. To attain proficiency in their use, effort and practice are required, but later the exercise of these skills gives us great satisfaction. Of all things invented by men, only numbers have never broken down.

This book uses chiefly two kinds of numbers. One kind consists of *scores,* which are obtained by counting, just as the score on a test is obtained by counting the number of correct answers. When you step on the bathroom scale, your score is the number of scale marks which pass under the pointer. In a race, there is one kind of score that is based on counting how many times the clock ticks and another that is based on counting the position or rank of each racer as he crosses the finish line. Every measurement is a score of some kind, and for scientific purposes it is most useful when the units counted are as nearly equal as we can make them.

The other kind of number which we shall use is a *statistic*. This is a number which is obtained by carrying out some systematic routine of calculation with a set of scores. It may be only to add them, or to divide each by 100, or it may be relatively complicated, like taking the square root of the sum of all their squares. Notice that by this definition, your "score" in an archery contest is a statistic, because to get it you do not simply count how many arrows strike in each ring of the target, but you multiply each count by an agreed point value and then add. Scores come directly from experience, but statistics interpret experience.

Changing scores into statistics sometimes requires a fair amount of computational labor. However, in this book our emphasis will be on the logic and the power of statistical methods and on the service they render to scientists. The routine business of computation will generally be passed over, to avoid distraction from the main points. We shall try to do an honest and thorough job in *explaining* WHY certain methods are useful, without dodging essential points, but we shall not take time to explain HOW they are used in practical detail. This omission should not be taken to imply that calculating is necessarily arduous or unpleasant work, as many people believe. Most of the calculations in statistics, other than mere additions, can be done quickly and almost effortlessly by slide rule. When greater accuracy is desired, logarithms may be called in. When there is a great volume of work, the electric calculator reduces it, and high-speed computers now perform in minutes programs of calculation which would otherwise consume months or years of a man's labor. It is important to realize that there are ways to manipulate numbers with ease, and no one should shy away from statistics because of the fear that it may be monotonous.

A better reason not to become a statistician would be dislike for people or for variety! A statistician ought to have a friendly disposition and a universal curiosity, because there will always be people knocking at his door, asking for help in planning research or in interpreting results.

In parts of this book, the reader will be asked to think harder than is customary in a book that is to be read for enjoyment. When the going seems rough, it is probably a good idea to drift with the current for a while, see where it is flowing, and then turn back a few pages to read again for deeper understanding. The choice, perhaps, is between rereading on your own option and repetitive restatement in the text. It seems the better plan that I should try to be economical in statement and that you should be generous in rereading, whenever that seems necessary. Of course I hope that when you finish the book you will want to read it all over again— as well as to read other books on the same subject—because you should then have discovered, if I have done my job passably well, that the study of statistics can be an exciting adventure.

CONTENTS

INTRODUCTION   This Thing about Numbers   v
1   The Place of Error in the World of Science   I
2   The Anatomy of Chance   10
3   Is It for Real?   25
4   Playing the Combinations   31
5   The Declaration of Dependence   40
6   What Can You Expect?   48
7   Talking about Types   59
8   Variations on a Chance Theme   66
9   Why Be Interested in Squares?   81
10 When Scores Are Indiscrete   100
11 The Extent of Reasonable Doubt   113
12 Ask the Improbable!   124
13 How to Tell a Misfit   132
14 Another Sign of Independence   142
15 Cause or Circumstance?   151
16 New Strategies for Science   164

APPENDIXES

A. The Zero Sum of Deviations   178
B. The Minimal Sum of Squares   179
C. The Variance Law   181
D. Variance of Binomial and Poisson Distributions   183
E. Small Samples   184
F. The Best-Fit Regression Line   185

INDEXES   189

THE
WORLD
OF
PROBABILITY

Chapter 1

THE PLACE OF ERROR
IN THE WORLD OF SCIENCE

●

SOME PEOPLE think they are always right. Such people would not be good scientists nor would they have any interest in statistics.

A scientist uses a microscope to study cells, a telescope to study stars, a cyclotron to study atomic particles—and statistics to study error. Each field of science has its own special instruments, but all scientists use statistics, because they must all contend with error.

Experimental science without error is as inconceivable as an ocean without salt. Each stream of fact which adds to our knowledge brings some error with it. In the lives of most men, according to a popular saying, "nothing is certain but death and taxes." The scientist adds "and empirical error." The most carefully regulated laboratory cannot eliminate it. One can no more lock error out of an experimental laboratory than one can lock bacteria out of a hospital. We must accept it as a fact of life and do something about it.

A statistician is a sleuth who hunts for error. Statistics is a tool for discovering it. Just as the study of viruses and bacteria has provided answers to some of the most basic

questions about the nature of life, so the study of error provides fresh points of view for the study of what scientists call
functional relationships—that is, the way in which measurable change in one phenomenon depends on measurable
change in another phenomenon.

The word "error" does not mean "mistake." The consequences of mistakes are a small and relatively uninteresting
source of experimental error. True, our instruments break
down; our eyes and ears play tricks on us; our measurements
are never exactly precise; sometimes even our arithmetic is
wrong. But if we attach too much importance to errors of
these kinds, we will never understand the true nature of
science and the true value of statistics. Experimental error is
something much more fundamental than an inaccurate measuring tape or an optical illusion. Since it is the first business
of statistics to help scientists analyze experimental error, we
must try to understand what it really is.

Whatever problem a scientist works on, it is sure to be
more complicated than he would like. Suppose he is measuring radioactive fallout at different latitudes. His results will
be influenced by the altitudes of the stations at which samples
are collected, by local rainfall, and by high-altitude storms
over a much wider area. If he is studying the opinions of
housewives about two brands of coffee, the answer he gets
from one woman may be changed because her husband was
grumpy at breakfast, and she would like to blame his mood
on the coffee. The results scientists get are always influenced
by such outside events, some of which they cannot possibly
foresee. For this reason, when an experiment is repeated, it is
very unusual to get exactly the same result twice. Experimental error is an inherent part of any genuine experiment.

Scientific observations typically are like the chatter on a
very noisy telephone connection. Or like holding a conversa-
tion in a low, cultured voice with someone on the other side
of a room filled with noisy people. What those other folks

are saying may also be very interesting, but it is not what we are trying to hear, and the crosstalk is deafening. The statistician must provide us with something like a directional microphone, in order to reduce the confusion.

We can describe the scientist's predicament in another way: when he studies a certain problem, the scientist is trying to measure the influence of X, or of X and Y, or even of X, Y, and Z. But there is a definite limit to the number of things he can take into account. Unfortunately, he is not able to prevent the simultaneous influence of still other factors, which we can call L, M, and N. The things he counts and measures are effects of both sets of influences. To the extent that they are effects of X, Y, and Z, they help to solve his problem, and to that extent they are information. To the extent that they are effects of other, accidental influences, they are error.

The same effect may be error or information, depending on the problem and the point of view. If a biologist wants to investigate how changes in nutrition influence growth, differences in hereditary constitution are a source of error; if he is studying the relation between heredity and stature, differences in nutrition are a source of error. If a physicist wants to study the relation between electrical conductance and temperature, differences in density of the conducting material are a source of error; if he studies the relation between density and conductance, temperature changes are a source of error. If an economist wants to learn how prices of commodities are influenced by changes in productivity, the effects of opening up new foreign markets will be a source of error; if he wants to study the effects of opening up new markets, changes in productivity are a source of error.

In each of these examples, it would not be possible to reach an accurate solution of the problem unless it were also possible to estimate the amount of error which is present—that is, the degree to which whatever we measure is influenced by other causes than those which are being investigated. Statistical methods are used to make such estimates.

An interesting illustration of how error and information may change places is provided by the contrast between the International Geophysical Year (IGY), which started in July 1957 and the International Years of the Quiet Sun (IYOS), which started in January 1964. The IGY was a history-making program of international scientific collaboration which was carefully planned to coincide with a period of maximum sun-spot activity, because of scientific interest in the effects of solar radiation. However, this "noisy sun" interfered with observations of certain other phenomena originating in outer space, and IYQS was planned to take advantage of an anticipated period of minimum sun-spot activity.*

Even a very accurate set of observations will contain a great deal of experimental error, that is, it will reflect a good many influences which lie outside the scope of inquiry at the time. This use of the word "error" may seem confusing, and it might seem preferable to say that the measured effects are contaminated by "unintended" or "unwanted" effects. However, scientists are touchy about words which might be taken to imply that they intended to have the results of their research come out one way or another, like the "research" mentioned in some television commercials. Another way to express the same idea is to classify the results of an experiment as due either to *design* or *accident*. We design the experiment to study certain influences, but accidental factors which we are not able to anticipate or control disturb the results by adding their own effects. Everyone knows that accidents upset the most careful designs of mice, men, and scientists. Mice and men gnash their teeth, but scientists calmly classify their frustrations as experimental error.

The difference between the effects of design and the effects

* See the article on IYQS by Martin Pomerantz, "International Years of the Quiet Sun," *Science*, 142 (1963), 1136–1143.

of accidental or chance causes is like the difference between the movements of a vessel at sea which is sailing on a planned course and one which is drifting aimlessly under the influence of changeable winds and currents. The movements of the second vessel can be described as random. It is not impossible that it may drift into some port, but more likely it will get nowhere in particular.

Statisticians use the word *random* to describe any phenomenon which is absolutely unpredictable from one moment to the next. Static interference with a radio message is random, and like experimental error it is most troublesome when the signal we are trying to receive is relatively weak. As we strain to hear the message, we can never know if the next instant will be one of blissful quiet or of ear-splitting noise. Cosmic radiation is a similar random phenomenon. These phenomena obey a statistical law called *Poisson's distribution,* which tells us how many short intervals and how many long intervals we can expect, but we can never know in advance whether the next interval will be long or short. Before cosmic rays were known to science, the same law was used (by Borkiewicz) to describe the frequency of deaths from kicks in cavalry divisions. This minor military hazard has been eliminated with the horses, but we can be sure that Poisson's spirit still rules over accidental dismemberment by tractor treads. Still another example is the appearance of vacancies on the Supreme Court bench, due to death or resignation of the justices.

One thing which all these phenomena have in common is that they are the results of causes which are so complicated that we cannot possibly keep track of them. Cosmic radiation, for example, consists of moment-to-moment effects of innumerable events which begin with the discharge of atomic particles in outer space, and are modified by the earth's magnetic field and the shielding effects of the atmosphere. Obviously, these effects cannot be predicted in detail. In a general way, they can be related to sun spots or to altitude, but it is absolutely impossible to say in advance how many times the Geiger counter will click during the next ten seconds.

Other statistical laws govern other kinds of random phenomena, such as the recombination of genes to determine hereditary characteristics, or the capture of particles by atomic nuclei, or the grade you get on an objective examination by pure guesswork, or the spread of an epidemic disease.

Examples like these serve to draw our attention to another important function of statistics. There are many different patterns of randomness, and each is associated with a certain pattern of cause. When we recognize that a phenomenon is random-like-this or random-like-that, we can often infer a good deal about the factors which determine it. There are processes which cannot be adequately described except by an analysis of error, in the statistical sense of the term. For example, the pressure of a gas on the walls of its container is the effect of a continual bombardment by the molecules which compose the gas, and it is not possible to describe their behavior except by statistical methods. The time required to develop a chain reaction in a radioactive pile is another problem of this sort. Statistical analysis is also used in a very different field of knowledge—modern literary criticism. Such elements of style as the frequency of short sentences, pronouns, or rhetorical questions are studied to solve problems of authorship. In this manner, it has been shown that many of the epistles credited to the apostle Paul were not written by him.

The error which results from unplanned effects in an experiment is sometimes systematic rather than random. Let us illustrate this difference. We said that local rainfall is one source of error which would influence measurements of radioactive fallout at different latitudes. If stations located in the northern region generally had more rain than those in the southern region, this would introduce a systematic error into the results. On the other hand, if there is no general tendency for more northerly stations to have either more or less rainfall, there will still be some error due to differences in local weather conditions from one station to another, but the error will be random rather than systematic.

Systematic error is more misleading than random error. A few pages back, we compared experimental error to interference in the reception of a radio message. Static interference, which is random, prevents us from hearing the message clearly, but it is not likely to cause us to imagine a different and misleading message. Interference from another radio station may provide a systematic musical accompaniment which is quite predictable from moment to moment, if you know the tune, but it may also cause us to misjudge the words or music of the program which we are trying to hear.

However, the detection of a systematic error often puts us on the track of a new discovery. A knowledge of the ways in which random errors behave helps us to recognize systematic errors and thus to eliminate them. What is equally important, it provides clues to the discovery of previously unsuspected influences. Pierre Laplace (1749–1827), a French astronomer who was one of the great pioneers in the application of what we now call statistical methods, drew attention to the possibilities of this approach. In his *Philosophical Essay on Probabilities,* Laplace tells how some of his important discoveries were initiated by recognition of nonrandom phenomena. For example, he calculated enormous odds—more than 4,000,000,-000,000 to 1—that these must be some "regular cause" responsible for the fact that all of the planets and their satellites revolve and rotate in approximately the same plane and direction. This is, of course, one of the basic facts to be considered in any theory of the origin of the solar system.

Modern astronomers have used the same approach in developing the theory of galactic systems. Early in this century, the Dutch astronomer J. C. Kapteyn stated a theory that all the stars in the heavens belong to two great streams, moving in opposite directions. This was his attempt to explain the fact that the movement of the stars in any cluster always seems to be predominantly in some directions, rather than haphazardly this way and that. (Remember that the clustering of stars depends only on the angle from which we view them and does not mean that they are actually near one another, even as astronomical distances are measured.) More recently, this effect has been better explained as due to the rotation of our own galaxy, that is, as a systematic error. The assumption that there is a random distribution of directions of star movement was thus re-established, and it continues to play an important part in theories of the structure and dimensions of the universe.

Indeed, the same kind of reasoning is commonplace in our daily affairs. How often do we make the remark, "That's no accident!" Whenever we are able to say this, either in everyday life or as a result of statistical analysis of scientific data, we are on the way to discovery.

Although statistical laws often seem to be a matter of pure mathematics, they might never have been developed if chance —in the form of games of chance—did not provide mathematicians with good practical material on which to begin the study of error. Error is all around us, but most of it is contaminated by human judgment, good or bad, or by some kindness of providence. In more sober terms, error is almost always at least a little systematic, and that makes it unsuitable for the development of elementary concepts of probability as a kind of pure luck. Before they could even conceive of probability as a problem for mathematical formulation, men first had to be confronted in their experience by instances of purely random error.

Games of chance provided the necessary empirical material, as well as the social motivation. This story has been told in an interesting way by F. N. David in a book called *Games, Gods, and Gambling.* In ancient pagan temples, "rolling bones" were used to forecast the will of the gods. The process of divination was often carried out with knucklebones, or with the heelbones of small animals. Each bone had six sides, but the sides were quite unequal, and only four were flat enough so that the bone could come to rest on them. That left plenty of room for the gods to intervene, or at any rate offered very little opportunity for men to reason about the results.

In time the rolling bones passed from the hands of priests into those of gamblers. They were replaced by carved ivories, and eventually they turned into the carefully polished cubes which we call dice. After a little experience, any observant player soon learns that one side of a perfectly balanced die has just as much chance of turning up as any other side. This takes the matter out of the hands of the gods and places it in the lap of "chance." Gamblers became aware that although the result of any single throw of the dice is unpredictable, still the throws in general obey laws which can be expressed as mathematical rules. However, it was not until the seventeenth century that algebra had advanced sufficiently so that it could make chance the object of serious mathematical study. Then chance was brought from heaven down to earth, where it became a part of the world of science.

Chapter 2

THE ANATOMY OF
CHANCE

●

IN EVERYDAY EXPERIENCE some things happen that seemed very unlikely beforehand, some things do not happen even though we have good reason to expect that they will, and some things can be explained only approximately. As scientists, we should like to believe that "Nothing happens without a cause, but everything for a reason and by necessity." That was a very advanced idea in the fifth century B.C., when Leucippus stated it, but it has been out of date since 1927, when the German physicist Werner Heisenberg demonstrated his startling principle of indeterminacy. On the basis of the quantum theory of physics, Heisenberg proved that science must deal with some events as matters of chance, not necessity.

As a practical matter, this has always been true. Causes can never be known in full detail, either because of their multiplicity or because of their minuteness. The Heisenberg principle conforms to a universal fact of life. No one believes that life is made up only of things which are sure to happen and that everything which has not happened must therefore have been impossible. When we do not think scientifically, we say that many things are a matter of luck. When we do think scientifically, we recognize that such events seem accidental only because things are so complicated that it is impossible to foresee all the consequences. It is really impossible, in the ultimate sense of the word, says Heisenberg, and therefore the quantum physicist must use statistical formulas to predict the behavior of atoms and to explain the progress of chemical reactions. Anyway, we all agree that it is impossible as a practical matter to trace all the trivial causes of vast events. An old story says, "for the want of a nail . . . the kingdom was lost." But today a Nobel prizewinner in physiology, J. C. Eccles, who has spent many years studying the chemical process by which one unit of the nervous system influences the next unit, tells us that crucial differences in behavior may sometimes hinge on a difference of a few molecules of some substance at a critical synapse, the point where this influence takes place.

After all, does not behavior sometimes depend on the toss of a coin, with all the uncertainties that attach to that most fickle event? Faced with a difficult problem, we may toss a coin for decision. At other times, we try to figure out the probabilities.

What is meant by a probability? When you flip a coin into the air to decide on a course of action, it is just as likely to fall heads as tails. Draw a card from a well-shuffled pack, and it is just as likely to be a heart as a spade, but it is more likely to be a numbered card than a face card. Drawing one card at poker, the odds are better if you are trying to complete a flush than if you are trying to fill an inside straight.

The probability of each of these events can be stated as a fraction. On the toss of a fair coin, the probability of heads equals $\frac{1}{2}$. Drawing from a deck of ordinary playing cards, the probability that the card will be a spade is $\frac{13}{52}$, while the probability that it will be an ace equals $\frac{4}{52}$. Holding four cards of one suit and discarding a card not of that suit, the probability is $\frac{9}{47}$ to complete the flush with the next card.

These calculations are based on a simple principle, which Laplace stated in this way:

> The theory of chance consists in reducing all events of the same kind to a certain number of equally possible cases—that is to say, such that we are equally uncertain about their existence—and in determining the number of cases favorable to the event whose probability we seek. The measure of this probability is the proportion of favorable cases to all the possible cases, that is, it is a fraction in which the numerator is the number of favorable cases and the denominator is the number of possible cases.

To determine a probability, we must perform three separate tasks: (1) Define a universe of equally possible cases, which includes all events of the kind we are interested in. We call it a universe because the whole problem will be solved inside it, without considering anything outside. Little or big, it is a world all its own, operating under laws which we proclaim. (2) Find out how big the universe is, that is, how many equally possible cases there are. Sometimes the universe is too big for counting, but if we can determine the relative frequency of different possible outcomes, that will do just as well. (3) Learn what proportion of all the cases in the universe "favor" the outcome which interests us.

We shall consider these steps in turn.

DEFINING THE UNIVERSE

The statistician's universe is imaginary, not real. We create it by our definition. We say: "Do thus and thus," and presto! we have created a universe which consists of all the possible results which "thus and thus" might produce. For example, say "Deal thirteen cards from a deck of playing cards," and, without even so much as rubbing a magic lantern, you have created a universe which consists of about 635,000,000,000 different bridge hands, all lurking inside the pack of cards with which you sit down to play. When the cards are dealt out, any one of these 635,000,000,000 hands is just as likely to appear as any other, and the only reason why thirteen spades seems like such a special event is because we usually overlook the fact that every "ordinary" hand is also 1 case in 635,000,000,000. There are also billions of "ordinary people" in the world, yet each person is a unique individual.

We must be careful to see that the universe which we have in mind is really one in which all cases are equally possible, since otherwise we will not be able to calculate a valid probability. This difficulty can be illustrated by a bit of history. A wealthy gentleman—probably the Grand Duke of Tuscany—complained to Galileo (1564–1642) that dice do not always behave as they should according to logic. He knew from experience—and it must have been a great deal of experience—that, in playing with three dice, 10 is an easier point to make than 9. This puzzled him, because there are just as many ways to get a sum of 9 as to get a sum of 10—or so he thought. He listed six combinations of pips on three dice which add up to 9, and six others which add up to 10.

Combinations Which Add to 9	Combinations Which Add to 10
6 + 2 + 1	6 + 3 + 1
5 + 3 + 1	5 + 4 + 1
5 + 2 + 2	5 + 3 + 2
4 + 4 + 1	4 + 4 + 2
4 + 3 + 2	4 + 3 + 3
3 + 3 + 3	6 + 2 + 2

Where, the Grand Duke asked Galileo, is the trouble?

The way in which the duke put his question shows that he understood the need for analysis in terms of equally possible cases. But he did not have a correct idea of the universe with which he was dealing, and therefore he was mistaken about the number of cases which it contained. Galileo showed him his mistake: it was in failing to keep track of each die separately. It is not just a matter of rolling three dice and adding their total, but rolling three dice and recording the result for each die. Now it is clear that there are $6 \times 6 \times 6 = 216$ possible outcomes, and the probability of each is $\frac{1}{216}$.

Galileo pointed out that any combination which consists of three different numbers (for example, 6, 2, and 1) can occur in six different arrangements; a combination which includes only two different numbers (for example, 4, 4, and 1) can occur in three different arrangements; while a combination in which only one number appears (like 3, 3, 3) has only one possible arrangement. By this analysis, he showed that of the 216 different arrangements which are possible with three dice, there are 25 which give a sum of 9, but 27 which give a sum of 10. Therefore the probability of throwing 9 equals $\frac{25}{216}$, which is just a little better than $\frac{1}{9}$, while the probability of throwing 10 equals $\frac{27}{216}$, which is exactly $\frac{1}{8}$.

The difficulty here was not in counting the cases, but in knowing what kind of cases to count, that is, in the definition of the universe. In statistical work we are always assuming equally possible cases, and if the assumption is not justified, the results will be false.

Another famous old problem sets a trap for a similar mistake. In modern form, it might go like this. I come home from the music shop with three new records. One has instrumental music on both sides, one has vocal music on both sides, while the third has instrumental music on one side and a vocalist on the other. The room is dark, so I cannot read the labels. I play the first side of one disc, which turns out to be instrumental. If I turn it over, what is the probability that the other side also will be instrumental?

Most people answer, in effect, "fifty-fifty." The justification for this answer goes like this: "The record which was played is either the one with one instrumental number or the one with two instrumental numbers; it is as likely to have been one as the other; one has instrumental music on the other side, the other has a vocalist; therefore there is a 50:50 chance that the other side of the record is instrumental." This argument sounds plausible but it is false, because the universe of the problem does not consist of three records but of six recordings. These six recordings include three different instrumental numbers, of which I have just played one; for two of these—on opposite sides of the same disc!—the other face is also instrumental, while for one it is not; therefore there are two chances in three that when I turn the record over, the other face will be instrumental.

If you are not solidly convinced, consider this variant, in which intuition supports reason in pointing to the correct answer. My house is burning, and I rush inside to save some valuable papers. There are in my closet two similar briefcases, one of which contains many valuable papers and one or two worthless sheets; the other contains many old papers which I had been planning to throw away, along with one or two valuable papers. I grab one briefcase, open it, and have only enough time to examine one paper before the smoke forces me to close my eyes. I must make my decision on the instant. I had just enough time to see that the paper I looked at was indeed valuable. Knowing that each sheet of paper—not just in one briefcase but in both briefcases, since I do not know which one I opened—had an equal chance to be the one which was examined, I decide that it is more probable that the briefcase in my hands is the one which holds many valuable papers. If, after all these heroics, I find out afterward that it contained mostly junk, I will be justified in feeling that my luck was extraordinarily bad and the result most improbable.

The logic behind this decision is often called the principle of *inverse probability,* because it reasons backward from an effect to its cause. We use this kind of reasoning every day of our lives. For example, if the rooters for one team leave a stadium tooting their horns and those of the other team are glum, there can be little doubt about who won the game. Thomas Bayes (1702–1761) was the first to show how an inverse probability could be calculated, but he felt so unsure about his results that this particular valuable paper was very nearly lost. Fortunately a friend found the right briefcase and published this paper after Bayes' death. Theoretical statisticians still do not agree whether his reasoning was sound, but there can be little doubt that the result is frequently useful. Those who reject his argument use another way to arrive at very much the same conclusions.

COUNTING THE UNIVERSE

After we know what the members of the universe are like, the next step is to determine how many of them there are. Usually it is not feasible to list all the cases, and so we need formulas. We shall consider several problems of this kind, starting with the simplest.

(1) If we throw two dice, there are 36 possible outcomes for each throw, but if we throw three dice, there are 216. Each of the dice has six sides, and the number of possible arrangements for three dice equals 6^3. In general, if there are m possible outcomes for each simple event and N parts to each compound event, then there are m^N distinguishable compound events.

(2) There are many situations in which the simple event has only two possible outcomes, like the toss of a coin. Suppose a psychologist wants to find out if a newborn chick can distinguish different shapes. He lets the chick peck at bits of paper instead of grain. Half of these simulated grains are tiny triangles, and the other half are circles with the same surface area. If the chick is allowed to take ten pecks at a ran-

domly mixed collection of the two shapes, the sequence of circles and triangles can take 1,024 different arrangements. It is as if each peck has two sides, just as each of the dice has six sides, and therefore the number of possible outcomes is 2^{10}, which equals 1,024. These are all "equally possible" cases. Ten successive pecks at triangles could happen just as easily, by chance, as triangle-circle-triangle-circle . . . in regular alternation. However, there are many different arrangements which include five triangles and five circles and only one which includes ten triangles.

Incidentally, in an experiment very much like this, it was shown that the chicks have a clear preference for circles, which proves that they do distinguish shapes. In real life in the barnyard, this preference probably helps them to peck at real grains instead of coarse gravel. Very similar experiments show that human infants prefer to look at certain patterns rather than others, and a pattern which is roughly like the human face—with two eyes and a mouth—is especially attractive almost as soon as the eyes open. These experiments disprove the theory that we must learn to see shapes, an idea for which Bishop Berkeley (1685–1753) argued so persuasively early in the eighteenth century that most psychologists have accepted it ever since. It takes experiments to prove that experience isn't everything.

(3) Each year, a queen and six princesses are chosen from the coeds at Pasadena City College to reign over the Tournament of Roses. When the selection committee has reduced the field to twenty-five finalists, there are still almost half a million possible selections of seven winners from the group. The method by which this calculation is performed is especially important for us, and we shall spend some time discussing it.

We use the symbol $\binom{N}{X}$ to stand for "the number of possible combinations of X objects which can be formed out of a population of N objects." For short, we can read the symbol as "take X of *N*." In this case, the problem is to "take 7 of 25." The universe, which we shall call a sample universe, consists of every possible combination which includes seven girls. There are 25 ways to make a first choice, then 24 ways to make a second choice, then 23 ways to make a third choice, and so on, until 18 girls remain unchosen. Therefore the number of possible arrangements in which seven choices can be made is the product of the numbers 25, 24, 23 . . . 19, inclusive. However, many of these arrangements are different ways of selecting the same seven girls in a different order. Any combination of seven girls can be chosen in $7 \times 6 \times 5 \times 4 \times 3 \times 2 \times 1 = 5050$ different orders or arrangements. So the answer to our problem is:

$$\binom{25}{7} = \frac{25 \times 24 \times 23 \times 22 \times 21 \times 20 \times 19}{7 \times 6 \times 5 \times 4 \times 3 \times 2} = 480,700.$$

As a practical matter, it is more convenient to write out such problems by using *factorial numbers*. For example, 7!, which we read *7-factorial*, stands for the product of 7 and each lower integer, down to and including 1. Using this convention, we are able to write a general formula:

$$\binom{N}{X} = \frac{N!}{X! \, (N - X)!} \, .$$

How this formula is derived is stated more fully in the next section.

(4) Another kind of universe with which we shall have to deal is the universe of possible comparisons which can be made whenever a sample from one population is to be compared with a sample from another population. For example, suppose that a survey compares the opinions of Democrats and Republicans on some national issue. In a statistical analysis of the results, one must consider the possibility that any similarly chosen sample of Democrats (that is, any one of a very large

number of possible outcomes of the same sampling procedure) might have been paired with any similarly chosen sample of Republicans (an item in another very large universe). Whatever difference exists between the two samples is a member of that still more numerous *universe of differences* which is made up of all these possible pairs. A statistician insists on seeing a forest in every tree, as if every tiny seedling had grown to maturity. He does not close his eyes to anything that might-have-been.

In a problem such as this, the universe of differences, and probably each universe of samples as well, is so large that precise counting is out of the question. The parent population from which the samples have been drawn has now given birth to so many children that we are almost in the position of the old woman who did not know what to do to take care of her numerous offspring. In this modern age, we are likely to ask how many children she must have in order to qualify for relief. We qualify for a special kind of relief from computational difficulties as soon as we are willing to declare that the universe is "infinite." At that point, it becomes possible to draw on the resources of the calculus. We shall see, when the time comes, that this mathematical bulldozer is capable of leveling mountains into molehills without changing their shape.

COMBINATIONS

Before turning to consider how we shall count "favorable" cases, let us give more careful attention to this question: How many combinations of X objects can be chosen from a population of N objects? We represent this number of combinations by the symbol $\binom{N}{X}$.

Consider first the number of ways to arrange X objects. There are X ways to select the first object, then $X - 1$ ways to select the second object, then X − 2 ways to select the third object, and so on, till only one object remains. Evidently the number of possible arrangements of X objects equals

$$X (X − 1) (X − 2) \ldots (1).$$

This series of factors, which includes every positive whole number up to and including X, is called X-*factorial,* and it is often represented by the symbol X!

Next consider the number of arrangements in which X objects can be chosen from among N objects. Now there are N ways to make the first choice, then $N − 1$ ways to make the second choice, then $N − 2$ ways to make the third choice, and so on, till X choices are made, and $N − X$ objects remain unchosen. Evidently there were $N − X + 1$ ways to make the Xth choice. Therefore the possible number of orders or arrangements for selecting X objects from among N objects equals

$$N (N − 1) (N − 2) \ldots (N − X + 1).$$

Among all these arrangements, each distinctive combination or set of X objects appears in X! different orders. Since we are interested only in distinctive sets, we must divide by X! Therefore,

$$\binom{N}{X} = \frac{N (N − 1) (N − 2) \ldots (N − X + 1)}{X!}.$$

The long line of factors in the numerator is not convenient to work with. If we multiply it by $(N − X)!$, it becomes $N!$ If we use the same multiplier in the denominator, the value of the fraction will not be changed. Taking advantage of this, we write:

$$\binom{N}{X} = \frac{N!}{X! \, (N-X)!}.$$

This is a convenient form, because it contains only factorial numbers, which means it can be solved quickly with the help of a table of the logarithms of factorials, even when N is quite large.

There will be many problems in which we shall need to "take X of N." Table 2-1 gives the answer for all cases where

TABLE 2-1. Pascal's Triangle. The number of distinctive combinations which include X successes, in N opportunities. Each entry is a value of

$$\binom{N}{X} = \frac{N!}{X! \, (N-X)!}.$$

X: NUMBER OF SUCCESSES	N: NUMBER OF OPPORTUNITIES										
	0	1	2	3	4	5	6	7	8	9	10
0	1	1	1	1	1	1	1	1	1	1	1
1		1	2	3	4	5	6	7	8	9	10
2			1	3	6	10	15	21	28	36	45
3				1	4	10	20	35	56	84	120
4					1	5	15	35	70	126	210
5						1	6	21	56	126	252
6							1	7	28	84	210
7								1	8	36	120
8									1	9	45
9										1	10
10											1
2^N	1	2	4	8	16	32	64	128	256	512	1024

N does not exceed 10. This table is called the *Pascal triangle*, after the great mathematician Blaise Pascal (1623–1662). Pascal was the first to make systematic use of these numbers to solve problems of probability by the method of analysis of combinations. Indeed, the history of probability, as a field of mathematical inquiry, starts with the correspondence which Pascal and Pierre de Fermat (1601–1665) carried on for a number of years.

It is worth playing a while with Pascal's triangle to become completely familiar with it. If you want to extend it farther, it is not necessary to calculate each new entry independently. Instead, you can use any of the following relationships:

(a) Taking any number in the table, if you add the number that stands just over it, you get the very next number on its own row. For example, $\binom{8}{3} = 35 + 21 = 56$.

(b) Moving down any column, each entry is equal to the preceding one multiplied by $(N - X + 1) / X$. For example, $\binom{8}{3} = (6/3)\ 28 = 56$.

(c) Moving along any row, each entry is equal to the preceding one multiplied by $N / (N - X)$. For example, $\binom{8}{3} = (8/5)\ 35 = 56$.

If you like problems in algebra, it is easy to prove each of these statements as a general rule, by writing out the formulas for

$$\binom{N}{X}, \binom{N}{X-1}, \text{ and } \binom{N+1}{X}$$

and comparing them.

COUNTING FAVORABLE CASES

The problem of deciding what is a favorable case is often a matter of judgment, which also rests on probabilities. Consider the case of the hungry chick pecking at imitation grain. We watch him peck ten times, and there are 1024 possible outcomes. They are all included in the Pascal triangle, in the column for 10 trials. There they are grouped according to the number of triangles (or of circles) in each series of 10 pecks. For instance, there are 10 ways in which just one triangle could occur along with nine circles, 45 ways for two triangles to occur with eight circles, 120 arrangements of three triangles and seven circles, and so on. Whatever may be the number of triangle pecks observed in any one sequence, the table tells us directly how many cases in the universe would have the same number. In the strict sense, this is all that is involved in "counting favorable cases."

However, what we want to know is whether the chick sees triangles as different from circles, and the only way he can tell us is by showing a clear preference for one or the other. What is a clear preference? Obviously, 6 out of 10 might be chance. What about 7 out of 10? Or 8 out of 10? At what point do we begin to feel that this is not chance but preference? How many of the possible outcomes in the universe are we willing to accept as favorable to the proposition that the chick does see form? Can we give any answer to this question?

Our answer must be based on the idea that we can accept the proposition that the chick sees shapes only if the way it behaves would be highly improbable on the contrary assumption, that it does not. If it pecks at 10 triangles in a row, or 10 circles, then we *know* it sees shapes, because each of these events will happen by chance only once in more than a thousand times. As a practical matter, it will defeat our purpose to insist on such a strict criterion (1,000 to 1 against the result being an accident), because we will find ourselves very rarely proving anything. In practice, scientists find it generally advisable to accept as *significant* (in a provisional way and subject to further checking) any result which would not happen more than 5 times in 100 by chance, and as *very significant* any result which would not happen more often than 1 time in 100 by chance. Let us look at the Pascal triangle, in the column $N = 10$, with these working criteria in mind.

Adding together entries at both ends of the column (because a preference for circles is just as convincing as a preference for triangles), we see that pecking 8 or more triangles or circles in a series of 10 pecks will occur in 11 per cent of possible cases (in 112 of 1024), but there are only about 2 chances in 100 (22 of 1024) that the 9 out of 10 criterion will be met by chance. In the latter case, it is reasonable to assume that the result is not due to experimental error.

This does not mean that a criterion of consistency must always be close to 90 per cent. If observations were based on a series of 20 pecks, there would be over one million possible cases, and of these, only about 4 per cent would show a disproportion as great as 15:5, in either direction. (If you want to verify this, you will have to fill in the first six entries for the column $N = 20$.) For a series of 100 pecks, a 60 per cent preference for either alternative would occur less than 1 time in 20 by chance.

This chapter has not described the entire anatomy of chance, but it has given the skeleton, the frame to which all the muscles must be attached. That skeleton is the idea of "combinatorial analysis," which is expressed compactly in the Pascal triangle.

Chapter 3

IS IT FOR REAL?

•

THE RULES of probability are unassailable as mathematical theorems, but there is always the question as to how well they work in real life. Years ago, Karl Pearson (1857–1936) discovered that the behavior of the roulette wheel in the famous gambling casino at Monaco did not conform to theoretical expectation. This result cast a darker shadow on the casino than on mathematics, but—unless we assume that the local sheet which published the data on the wheel's performance deliberately eliminated many long runs as too improbable—the fact remains that anyone who undertook to predict the behavior of that roulette wheel on the basis of theoretical expectations would have had some unpleasant surprises.

The empirical testing of probability theory is the best way to test the limits of its application. The Grand Duke, Galileo's patron, was not foolish when he complained that the dice did not behave according to logic, even though he was mistaken. It is always a useful exercise to compare fact and theory.

As theory, we shall take the predictions based on the Pascal triangle. These predictions apply to any series of two-sided events in which the probabilities of success and failure are equal. For example, they tell us the expected relative frequencies of heads and tails when a certain number of coins are tossed together. If five coins are tossed, the column for $N = 5$ tells us the expected relative frequencies of instances in which 5 heads appear, or 4 heads, or 3 heads, and so on. This is also the expected distribution of boys in families with five children, on the assumption (which is not quite accurate) that male and female births are equally likely. If that assumption were correct, among mothers who gave birth to five children, 1 in 32 would have five boys, while 1 other would have five girls. Twelve of such mothers, or 3 in 8, would have at least four children of the same sex, male or female. Before going on, verify these statements in the Pascal triangle.

If we expect that we will find in experience the exact frequencies which exist in Table 2–1, we are almost sure to be disappointed. This would be so even if results were due to pure chance, without a systematic bias. To give a fuller idea of how chance works, we shall perform a *sampling experiment.* We shall compare the expected values in the Pascal triangle with actual samples, drawn by chance. For example, what kind of a picture of chance would we get, if we were to toss coins, instead of relying on a mathematical formula?

There was a time when flipping coins might occupy almost as much of a statistician's time as rolling dice. However, this is just one more instance in which technological improvements have displaced time-honored occupations. Now we can get the same results more easily and faster by using a table of random digits—a table in which all the digits appear over and over in helter-skelter fashion, without any predictable order.

It is not easy to write digits in this fashion, because the human mind cannot operate randomly. One way to get a random series of digits is to calculate a great many places for the value of some transcendental number like π, the ratio of the circumference of a circle to its diameter, or e, the natural base of logarithms. These values have recently been calculated to 100,000 places and 60,000 places, respectively. In each case the sequence of digits is completely random, because it is impossible to make any prediction about what the next digit will be by looking at those that have gone before. Most tables of random digits are made with the help of some mechanical device like a roulette wheel, which gives every digit an equal chance to appear in every position in the table —except that even the machinery, as it wears down, begins to have nonrandom habits.

In our daily experience, perhaps the closest thing to really random digits is the last few places of telephone numbers. (Obviously, the digits which represent the exchanges are far from random.) The randomness will be further improved if the columns of digits in a large telephone directory are read vertically instead of horizontally. So if you want to repeat the experiment which is about to be described or one of those which will appear later in the book, you can do so by opening at random to any page in the telephone directory.

A table of random digits is pure error, and with ingenuity it can be made to simulate any kind of chance situation. One can use random digits to solve problems which are too complex to be handled in any other way. This has been nicknamed the "Monte Carlo method," taking the name from the famous gambling casino at Monaco. This randomizing method has become so popular that a few years ago a research organization, The RAND Corporation, published a huge volume which includes one million random digits, to assist those who want to use the Monte Carlo method on numerous or extensive problems. Radar defense crews, for example, are trained in practice situations which are constructed with the help of random digits, to provide better simulation of true combat conditions than would be possible in an artificially conceived problem. M. S. Bartlett, a British statistician, has used the Monte Carlo method to show how the recurrent pattern of epidemics in certain diseases depends on such factors as the rate of infection, rate of recovery, amount of travel between different countries or different parts of a country, and changes in susceptibility to infection after recovery from the disease.

We shall use random digits as a quick, clean, and quiet substitute for flipping coins. To do this, we merely agree to regard each odd digit as a head, and each even digit (including zero) as a tail. Instead of flipping five coins, we look at a series of five digits and count how many odd digits are included. I have just done this for 320 groups of 5 digits, selected from a page of The RAND Corporation volume, and the results appear in Table 3-1. They are tabulated separately

TABLE 3-1. This is a record of a sampling experiment, in which the number of odd digits was recorded for successive groups of five digits in a table of random digits. Each column, from *A* to *J*, gives results for 32 successive groups.

Odd Digits	*A*	*B*	*C*	*D*	*E*	*F*	*G*	*H*	*I*	*J*	Total
5	1	0	2	0	2	0	3	1	2	0	11
4	6	6	3	4	3	8	5	6	5	3	49
3	12	11	14	12	13	6	12	10	8	14	112
2	9	8	7	12	5	12	8	11	9	10	91
1	3	5	5	2	6	5	3	4	8	5	46
0	1	2	1	2	3	1	1	0	0	0	11
Total Odd	86	78	83	78	77	79	90	85	80	79	815

for each series of 32 groups, which makes it easy to compare the results with the theoretical expectation in the Pascal triangle.

Not once do we find, for 32 successive groups of 5, the 1–5–10–10–5–1 distribution which is "expected." For all the groups together, we do not get the "expected" distribution of 10–50–100–100–50–10. Well, such is chance! The more we study it, the more we learn that chance *means* unpredictability, within limits. If we could know in advance what the results would be, they would not be chance. Nevertheless, the theoretical expectation is fulfilled in certain limited respects. For example, in every series the combined frequency of 2 heads and 3 heads is greater than the combined frequency for 0, 1, 4, and 5 heads. In every case the total for 1 and 4 is greater than for 0 and 5. Clearly, there is a trend toward what is "expected."

How long would we have to continue this sampling to establish this trend beyond question? James Bernoulli (1654– 1705) proved that in any case of this sort, if we just go on taking trials long enough, we can get just as close as we please to the expected proportions in the various categories. His theorem is sometimes called "the law of large numbers." It implies that a very big sample, if it is truly random, must closely resemble the universe out of which it is taken. But the test of resemblance is a matter of *proportions,* not of frequencies. No amount of random experience can be expected to give exact expected frequencies. Although the proportional discrepancies will get smaller and smaller, it is just as certain that the frequency discrepancies will get bigger and bigger. We cannot have more experience except at the price of more error. If we had 3,200 cases instead of 320, the proportions in the various categories would be closer to expectation, but it is virtually certain that the numerical differences from the expected frequencies would be much greater. As a matter of fact, we could expect, with 10 times as many trials, that the frequency discrepancies would increase approximately by a factor of $\sqrt{10}$, or a little more than 3 times. Obviously this would reduce the proportion discrepancies to only about a third of what they were in this experiment.

This contrast between frequencies and proportions is at the bottom of the paradox which traps so many people who reason that after a run of heads it is good to bet on tails, or, after a run of red on the roulette wheel, to bet on black, because things just have to even out in the long run. They do, but only in the proportionate sense, not in the frequency sense. If, for the toss of a coin, the probability of heads equals ½, it remains ½ for each toss and for any future series of tosses, even after a long run of tails. What the law of large numbers asserts is that the accumulated excess of tails will become trivial and inconsequential in a proportionate sense when a great many more tosses will have been made. It does not promise a complementary excess of heads to balance the score. A good part of the profit of the professional gambler must come from his complacent stand-pat position, buttressed by the unvarying laws of chance, while his amateur customers increase their bets because they feel sure it is time for a change.

There is still another way to define expectation in this situation. Since the probability of an odd digit equals ½, we "expect" that half of the digits selected will be odd. This means that we "expect" the quite impossible number of 2.5 odd digits in each group of 5. Although this seems an unusual use of the word "expect," it is a useful one, for it also tells us to expect 80 odd digits in each set of 32 groups and 800 in the entire experiment. In the bottom row of Table 3-1 you can see to what degree these expectations were fulfilled.

This short chapter has combined an empirical test of the basic theory of probability, as applied to a very simple situation, with a discussion of the so-called "law of large numbers." Theory and experience "agree to disagree": that is, they both indicate that statistical predictions must always be regarded as approximate, not exact.

Chapter 4

PLAYING
THE COMBINATIONS

●

EACH ENTRY in Pascal's triangle is for a compound event of a special kind—an event which can turn out either "this way" or "that way," which has been observed on N occasions, and which turned out "this way" X times. Consequently, it turned out "that way" $N - X$ times. The table tells us how many equally possible combinations of simple events can lead to such a compound event. If the simple event is of such a nature that "this way" is just as probable as "that way"—like the two sides of a fair coin—then all the cases in each column of the table are equally possible in the sense intended by Laplace. Under such conditions, each entry in the table may be regarded as the numerator of a probability, for which the total of the column in which it appears is the denominator (for example, 252/1024).

In Table 4-1 we start by listing all the possible scores for a 5-part compound event. Then, from Pascal's triangle, we write down the number of ways in which it is possible to arrive at each of these scores. We restate the frequencies as fractions of their total and the fractions as proportions. The final column of expected proportions constitutes a *probability*

TABLE 4-1. The calculation of probabilities for various possible outcomes of a 5-part compound event, when *p*, the probability of success, equals ½ for each simple event.

X	$\binom{5}{X}$	$\binom{5}{X}(1/2)^5$	$P\{X\}$
5	1	1/32	.03125
4	5	5/32	.15625
3	10	10/32	.31250
2	10	10/32	.31250
1	5	5/32	.15625
0	1	1/32	.03125
	32	32/32	1.00000

distribution for all the possible outcomes of any 5-part compound event, when there is a 50:50 probability of success for each simple event of which it is composed.

In the future (as in Table 4-1) we shall use small *p* to represent the probability of a simple event, but we shall write large *P* to stand for the probability of a compound event. Therefore small *p*'s will always stand either for a priori assumptions or for the proportion of successes found in actual experience, while large *P*'s stand for calculated probabilities. In either case, the event to which a probability applies may be indicated by a symbol or a numerical value enclosed by braces, as in the heading of the last column of Table 4-1.

This probability distribution would apply, for example, to the sex of five successive births in a public hospital, on the assumption that male and female births are equally likely. The column for $N = 7$, in the Pascal triangle, can be converted in the same manner into a probability distribution for the number of blondes in the court of the Tournament of Roses, on the assumption that blondes and brunettes have, in the aggregate, equal chances of being chosen. The column for $N = 10$ can be converted into a probability distribution for chance scores on a class quiz which consists of ten true–false questions, where the probability of guessing each correct answer is ½.

All these compound events are alike in being composed of simple events for which $p = $ ½. But what if you are confronted with a multiple-choice examination, with five choices on each question? In that case, $p = $ ⅕. What if the gentlemen of the selection committee distinctly prefer blondes? What if, as was first observed many years ago, baby boys are really born more often than baby girls, even though by a slight margin? When the probability of a "success" in each simple event is either more or less than ½, an additional complication enters into the calculation of the probability distribution. To understand it, we shall have to consider the nature of compound probabilities more closely.

The calculation of compound probabilities is based on a principle which is so nearly obvious that it is often called an axiom. If two events are independent—which means that the way one turns out does not influence the way the other turns out—then the probability that both will happen is the product of their separate probabilities. If Joe McSwat, batting .375, comes up after Tommy Thump, batting .320, then the probability that they will both get hits equals the product of those two proportions, which is .12. In symbols:

$$P \{\text{A and B}\} = p \{\text{A}\} \cdot p \{\text{B}\}.$$

This so-called *multiplication law* can be extended to include any number of independent events which are to be combined into a compound event. For example, suppose I am about to order soup, entree, and dessert from a menu which lists 2 soups, 5 entrees, and 4 desserts. If each choice is made independently and by chance, the probability that I will order tomato soup, fried chicken, and ice cream equals ½ × ⅕ × ¼ = ¹⁄₄₀.

Each probability in Table 4-1 is really based on a calculation of that kind, but since each simple event (success or

The World of Probability

failure, indifferently) has the same probability, all the answers come out as multiples of $(\frac{1}{2})^5$. When success and failure are not equally likely, it is no longer true that each compound event is equally likely. Then we must pay special attention to how many successes and how many failures are included in each compound event.

To illustrate this, we shall take a problem of the kind which interested a number of distinguished mathematicians who were eager to show that the theory of probability had social significance beyond its moral lessons on the futility of gambling. Let us suppose that the guilt or innocence of an accused man is to be decided by a bench of judges. The evidence is conflicting, but we will assume that there are 2 chances in 3 that a sincere and learned judge will reach a "just" rather than an "unjust" decision. What is the advantage to the cause of justice in having more than one judge deliberate on the case?

Table 4-2 gives the solution to this problem in the case of three judges. There are eight ways in which the decisions of the individual judges can be combined into a majority verdict, but these are no longer "equally possible" ways. For

TABLE 4-2. Possible combinations of decisions by three judges, and the joint probability of each combination when p, the probability of a "just" decision by each individual judge, equals 2/3.

DECISIONS BY THE INDIVIDUAL JUDGES			PROBABILITIES OF THE SIMPLE EVENTS			JOINT PROBABILITY
I	II	III				
Just	Just	Just	(2/3)	(2/3)	(2/3)	8/27
Just	Just	Unjust	(2/3)	(2/3)	(1/3)	4/27
Just	Unjust	Just	(2/3)	(1/3)	(2/3)	4/27
Unjust	Just	Just	(1/3)	(2/3)	(2/3)	4/27
Just	Unjust	Unjust	(2/3)	(1/3)	(1/3)	2/27
Unjust	Just	Unjust	(1/3)	(2/3)	(1/3)	2/27
Unjust	Unjust	Just	(1/3)	(1/3)	(2/3)	2/27
Unjust	Unjust	Unjust	(1/3)	(1/3)	(1/3)	1/27
						27/27

example, the probability for coincidence of three "just" decisions equals $(\frac{2}{3})^3 = \frac{8}{27}$, while the probability for coincidence of three "unjust" decisions equals $(\frac{1}{3})^3 = \frac{1}{27}$. Similarly, the probability for any combination which includes two
just decisions equals $(\frac{2}{3})^2(\frac{1}{3}) = \frac{4}{27}$; for combinations which
include only 1 just decision, the probability is $(\frac{2}{3})(\frac{1}{3})^2 = \frac{2}{27}$.

If we are not to abandon the basic concept of probability
as a proportion of equally possible cases, we must find such a
universe somewhere beneath all these calculations. Now we
remember that the probability distribution is based on the
operation of chance, not on the learning and sincerity of the
judges. In a completely chancy world fate marks the ballots,
and blindfolded judges select them. So we translate the situation into those terms by saying that each judge puts his hand
into a cap which contains three ballots, of which two are
inscribed with an "unjust" and one with a "just" decision. The
problem is precisely similar to the one which Galileo solved
for the Grand Duke. Each judge has three choices, which now
are equally possible, and these can be combined in twenty-
seven equally possible ways. However, all this requires no
attention from us, once we are satisfied that the fundamental
schema of probability is, in fact, intact. Before going on, let
us note in passing that Table 4-2 shows that with three judges
the probability for a just majority verdict equals $\frac{20}{27}$, or
approximately .74.

It would be very awkward to follow this method for larger
problems. To list the possible combinations for five judges
would take thirty-two lines, and it would take more than half
of this book to list all the possible combinations for a jury of
twelve men. Fortunately, we can shorten the work a great deal
by taking advantage of the fact that each compound event
which includes the same number of successes also has the same
probability. To do this, we proceed as follows:

In a memorandum column which will not enter directly
into the calculation of probabilities, we list all the possible

scores, or values of X, from 0 to *N,* inclusive. Then, on each row, for the given value of X, we write these three factors, whose product is the probability of that score:

(1) The number of ways in which one can "take X of *N.*" This number is taken directly from the Pascal triangle.

(2) The joint probability of X successes, in any order. This equals p^X.

(3) The joint probability of $N - X$ failures, in any order. This equals $(1 - p)^{N-X}$. It is customary to let *q* stand for the probability of a failure, or $1 - p$. Making this substitution, the entire procedure is stated in this equation:

$$P\{X\} = \binom{N}{X} p^X q^{N-X}.$$

Table 4-3 shows how the formula is applied. Each factor in the equation appears as the heading of a column in the table.

TABLE 4-3. Calculation of probabilities for various possible outcomes of the deliberative process, where X stands for the number of "just" decisions by individual judges, with five judges deliberating, when *p,* the probability of a just decision by each individual judge, equals 2/3.

X	$\binom{5}{X}$	p^X	q^{5-X}	$P\{X\}$
5	1	$(2/3)^5$	$(1/3)^0$	32/243
4	5	$(2/3)^4$	$(1/3)^1$	80/243
3	10	$(2/3)^3$	$(1/3)^2$	80/243
2	10	$(2/3)^2$	$(1/3)^3$	40/243
1	5	$(2/3)^1$	$(1/3)^4$	10/243
0	1	$(2/3)^0$	$(1/3)^5$	1/243
				243/243

First there is the memorandum column of values for X. Then, since $N = 5$, a column copied out of the Pascal triangle, showing on each row how many ways there are to "take X of 5." Next, on each row, come p^X, followed by q^{N-X}. Each probability is the product of three such factors. However, since the denominator on every row equals $3^5 = 243$, that need be calculated only once. It is the numerators that differ: 2^5 on one row, 5 (2^4) on the next, 10 (2^3) on the next, and so forth. Finally, the sum of probabilities tells us that all 243 "equally possible cases" have been accounted for.

We see that with five judges, the probability of a just verdict rises to 192/243, or .79. If there were twenty-one judges, and each reached an independent decision, the proportion of just verdicts would rise above .94. This does not mean that increasing the number of judges is a sure road to perfect justice. The difficulty is that, as we increase the number on the bench or the size of a committee, it becomes less and less likely that the individual members really will reach independent decisions. This problem also is amenable to statistical investigation, but to pursue it now would take us too far afield. However, you might like to consider how to formulate the reduced likelihood of an independent decision, as each judge is exposed to an increasing number of social pressures from his peers.

If you have studied advanced algebra, you will recognize that the method we have been using is the same one which is used to determine the value of any binomial (that is, a sum of two numbers) when it is raised to an integral power. For this reason, probability distributions which can be calculated in this way are called *binomial probability distributions,* and the Pascal triangle is often called the *table of binomial coefficients.* In a binomial probability distribution, the binomial is $p + q$. Since $p + q = 1$, the value of $(p + q)^N$ must always equal 1, no matter what value N may have. In other words, the sum of the probabilities must always add up to the certainty that *something* will happen, and this provides a convenient check on our calculations. We are not making use of the binomial expansion in order to learn the value of $(p + q)^N$, but in order to break that value down into its parts, because each part arises from one of the possible ways of combining p's and q's (successes and failures) in the universe defined, and therefore each is the probability associated with a certain number of "successes."

Table 4-4 shows how the formula can be used to make a

TABLE 4-4. Calculation of probabilities for the number of boys, X, in a family of five children, assuming that p, the probability of a male birth, equals .514.

X	$\binom{5}{X}$	$.514^X$	$.486^{5-X}$	$P\{X\}$
5	1	.036	1.	.036
4	5	.070	.486	.170
3	10	.136	.236	.321
2	10	.264	.114	.303
1	5	.514	.056	.143
0	1	1.	.027	.027
				1.000

probability distribution for the expected number of boys in families with five children, taking account of the fact that at birth boys consistently outnumber girls in the ratio of 18:17. (No more do we suppose, as some did in the eighteenth century, that this is a violation of chance and a proof that man's welfare is regulated by a divine plan. We now know that boys are conceived in much greater numbers than girls, but they succumb more readily to the rigors of life—even life in the womb. Truly a weaker sex, they lose most of their advantage by the time of birth, and at every age have a lower life expectancy than their sisters.)

When the problem is stated to take account of this inequality, the universe of equally possible cases includes $35^5 = 52,521,875$ members, but it is quite unnecessary for us to concern ourselves with them in detail. We carry out the calculations with $p = .514$ and $q = .486$, and it is all a very simple matter if you learn to use a log-log slide-rule, or an electric calculator, but somewhat tedious with paper and pencil. You have probably already noticed, in the previous example, that when p is not equal to q, the probability distribution is not symmetrical. This is true again in the present case.

One purpose of preparing such a distribution is to test whether the theoretical expectation agrees with experience. If so, sex distribution among children in the same family is wholly a matter of chance. If not, nonchance influences are present, and it is reasonable to suppose that some mothers (or fathers) have a tendency to give birth to boys rather than girls, or the reverse. We will come back to this problem in Chapter 13, and then we shall see that although chance plays the greatest part in determining sex, a small nonchance influence can be demonstrated.

Before leaving the binomial distribution, it is of interest to point out that in such a distribution, when you know the probability of one score, you can calculate the probability of the next higher score from this relationship:

$$P\{X\} = \frac{p}{q} \cdot \frac{N - X + 1}{X} \cdot P\{X - 1\}.$$

In this formula, the factor p/q expresses the effect of "one more success, one failure less," and the factor $(N - X + 1)/X$ takes care of the shift to the next entry in the same column of the Pascal triangle. We will use this relationship at a later point (see Chapter 8), when we develop a special formula for dealing with very small probabilities.

Of course, it is equally possible to run down the scale instead of up. In that case, the formula is:

$$P\{X\} = \frac{q}{p} \cdot \frac{X + 1}{N - X} \cdot P\{X + 1\}.$$

Chapter 5 will deal with two important applications of binomial probability distributions in scientific research.

Chapter 5

THE DECLARATION
OF DEPENDENCE

●

SOME THINGS ARE often joined in experience, like smoke and fire, blonde hair and blue eyes, or cigarette smoking and lung cancer. The investigation of such contingent relationships often leads to a better understanding of the influences which determine these events, although one must be wary of assuming that one phenomenon is the cause of the other. We make no assumptions about the directness or the direction of causal relationship when we call such pairs of phenomena interdependent in a probabilistic sense.

Two events are called *independent* if the probability of one is not affected by whether the other happens or not. The probability distributions in Chapter 4 dealt only with compound events made up of independent events. Sometimes, however, the probability of one event changes because another event takes place. Such an event is *dependent* on the other, and we say that its probability is *conditional*.

A trivial example will help to make the concept clear. There is a 20 per cent probability that Prof. Blinks will go to Europe next year if his request for a sabbatical leave is not approved, but there is an 80 per cent probability that he will make the trip if the request is approved. The probability that the request will be approved is 60 per cent. These assumptions lead to the following distribution of probabilities for all the possible compound events:

Sabbatical and travel	(.60) (.80) =	.48
Sabbatical without travel	(.60) (.20) =	.12
No sabbatical, but travel	(.40) (.20) =	.08
No sabbatical, no travel	(.40) (.80) =	.32
		1.00

There is nothing really new in this procedure, but to include the concept of conditional probability the multiplication law can be given this more general form: *The probability of a compound event is the product of the probability of one event and the conditional probability of the other, on the condition that the first event occurs.*

$$P \{A \text{ and } B\} = p \{A\} \cdot p \{B \text{ if } A\}.$$

An interesting application of this concept is made in genetics, in studying the inheritance of certain rare diseases which are due to recessive genes. Bear in mind that if a child receives such a gene from each of his parents he will become a victim of the disease; if he receives the gene from only one parent, he will be safe from the disease, but he will transmit the recessive gene to approximately one-half of his own children. They will be safe unless they receive another recessive gene from the other parent.

For this example, let us suppose that the proportion of dominant, disease-averting genes for this condition is .98, and the proportion of recessive, disease-bearing genes is .02. These are not the proportion of people with and without such genes, but the proportions of dominant and recessive genes distributed in the "gene population." The probability distribution for recessive genes, as they occur in people, is the binomial distribution for $p = .98$ and $N = 2$. This is:

$$
\begin{array}{llll}
\text{No recessive genes,} & p^2 & = & .9604 \\
\text{One recessive gene,} & 2pq & = & .0392 \\
\text{Two recessive genes,} & q^2 & = & .0004 \\
\hline
& & & 1.0000
\end{array}
$$

We can avoid an unnecessary complication, which has very little influence on the outcome, if we assume that the disease is mild enough or appears late enough so that it does not seriously reduce chances of parenthood. Under these conditions, and with random mating in the population at large, 1 child in 2,500 will receive two recessive genes and thus fall victim to the disease.

Now consider the situation in a marriage between first cousins. This means that the husband and wife have one set of grandparents in common. *If* the husband carries the recessive gene, there is 1 chance in 2 (a conditional probability) that he got it from this set of grandparents; *if* he did, there is again 1 chance in 2 (another conditional probability) that a similar gene was transmitted to the wife's parent and still again 1 chance in 2 that it was passed on to that other grandchild who is now his wife. The net effect of this chain of conditional probabilities is that when either member of a first-cousin marriage carries a recessive gene, there is 1 chance in 8 that the other does too. Therefore the probability that both mates in a marriage of first cousins possess the recessive gene is $(\frac{1}{8})(2pq)$. The joint probability that a given child of the marriage will receive two such genes, one from each of his parents, is one-fourth of that, or $pq/16$. Instead of 1 child in 2,500 being afflicted, as in the general population, the rate rises to 1 in 1,225.

The most conspicuous example of this effect, and the one which first attracted attention, is the high rate of deaf-mutism in isolated communities where a good deal of inbreeding has taken place. At the other end of the social ladder, the frequency of hemophilia in some royal families of Europe is a penalty they pay for their overly exclusive marital customs. Whenever a developmental defect has been identified, the question whether it has a hereditary or an environmental basis can frequently be answered by comparing the rate at which it appears in the general population and the rate among children of first-cousin marriages.

Geneticists make an even more important use of the concept of conditional probability for studying the location of particular genes on chromosomes. This application depends on the fact that chromosomes come in pairs, and although each parent usually transmits one whole chromosome of each pair to each of the offspring, sometimes the chromosomes break up and rejoin in such a way that a new one is formed which is neither wholly from one parent nor from the other, but partly from each. Now, suppose that a strain of fruit flies is developed which is completely dominant for two characters carried by separate genes located on one chromosome, and another strain is recessive for these same characters. In cross-breeding, if one dominant character appears without the other in some of the offspring, it is because the chromosomes split at a point between the location of these genes. If such a split takes place, it is more likely to fall between two genes which are far apart than between two which are close together. Therefore the conditional probability of "crossing over," which is the name given to this phenomenon, is a function of the distance between the genes. From a study of the relative frequency of crossing over in different pairs of traits, Thomas Hunt Morgan and his co-workers were able to prepare detailed charts showing the positions of the various genes on each chromosome, in the fruit fly. This was an important part

of the evidence which convinced scientists that the genes were
real, not imaginary.

As in these examples, the application of statistics in
genetics typically requires large numbers of observations. By
contrast, there is another application of the binomial distribution and the concept of conditional probability, which is
especially valuable in dealing with experimental evidence
where there is a very small number of observations. As an
example of this, we shall take the data of an experiment which
deals with the effects of physiological stress on resistance to
poliomyelitis (infantile paralysis).

It is not a new idea that in order to meet stress successfully
in later life one must become accustomed to a certain amount
of it in early experience. This general idea has found an interesting application in modern medicine as a result of the work
intiated by Hans Selye of McGill University on the concept of
stress as a way in which the body reacts to unaccustomed
stimulation. The experiment we are considering is one of a
number which show that the experience of stress may increase
the body's ability to resist disease.

In this experiment twenty-three monkeys were the subjects,
and the stress situation was one in which the experimental
animals had to work diligently at a learned task, because
whenever they let up, they received a painful electric shock.
All of the monkeys in the experiment were similarly inoculated
with the virus of Type I polio. The experimental animals
received the inoculation immediately after twenty-four hours
of their stress experience. Almost all of the animals became ill,
and most of them died within a few days, but there was a
marked difference between experimental and control animals
in the rate of survival. As shown in Table 5-1, only 1 of the
11 control animals, but 7 of the 12 experimental animals,
came through their illness successfully. These are the data we
wish to analyze.

In order to do this, we set up an "hypothesis of independ-

TABLE 5-1. The effect of stress on resistance to poliomyelitis infection.

	SURVIVED	DIED	TOTAL
Experimental monkeys	7	4	11
Control monkeys	1	11	12
	8	15	23

Source: James T. Marsh, John F. Lavender, Shueh-Shen Chang, and A. F. Rasmussen, "Poliomyelitis in Monkeys: Decreased Susceptibility after Avoidance Stress," *Science*, 140 (1963), 1414–1415.

ence." This hypothesis asserts that it really makes no difference whether stress did or did not precede the inoculation and that it is just a matter of chance that a higher proportion of animals survived in one group than in the other. To test this hypothesis, we need to calculate the probability that such a difference could have come about by chance.

Among all the animals, 8 of 23 survived. This means that there were 490,314 different ways (take 8 of 23) to reach this result.

Among the experimental animals, 7 of 11 survived, and among the control animals, 1 of 12. There are 330 ways to take 7 of 11, and 12 ways to take 1 of 12. Therefore, by the multiplication law, there are 3,960 ways to reach the total of eight survivors, by combinations which preserve the distinction between experimental and control animals. The probability of obtaining this result by chance is 3,960/490,314, or .0081.

We must also consider the probability that chance might have brought about an even more extreme result. In this case, there is only one more extreme result to consider: the possibility of having no survivors among the control animals, and all eight among the experimental animals. Since there is only 1 way to take 0 of 12, and 165 ways to take 8 of 11, the probability of this outcome equals 165/490,314, or .0003. Adding this to the previous answer, the joint probability for both outcomes equals .0084. Thus there is less than 1 chance in 100 that, with eight survivors in all, the experiment might have turned out so favorably to the stressed animals. This leads us to set aside the hypothesis of independence as untenable, and we conclude that there is a statistical dependence between the experience of shock and resistance to the infection. However, we acknowledge that there is still a slim possibility that this is a chance effect, and therefore we say that this judgment is made "at the 99 per cent level of confidence."

This method was introduced by Ronald A. Fisher (1890–1962), whose name we shall meet again, and it is usually called "Fisher's exact test." If the cells of a fourfold table are labeled thus:

$$A \quad B$$
$$C \quad D$$

the procedure which we have followed is stated in the following formula:

$$P = \binom{A + B}{A} \binom{C + D}{C} \div \binom{A + B + C + D}{A + C}.$$

For convenience, this can be restated in this form:

$$P = \frac{(A + B)! \, (C + D)! \, (A + C)! \, (B + D)!}{A! \, B! \, C! \, D! \, (A + B + C + D)!}.$$

Fisher's test is one example of an important development in modern statistics, which helps to make scientific labor more productive: the appearance of methods which enable us to base a conclusion on a small body of evidence. The same method would be awkward to apply with large numbers or to a distribution of data which made it necessary to consider a good many "more extreme" outcomes. In later chapters we shall learn about approximation methods which are quite satisfactory under those conditions. They will be based on special probability distributions which are derivative from the binomial distribution but have their own distinctive characteristics.

We shall resume our discussion of probability distributions in Chapter 8. Chapters 6 and 7 will be concerned for the most part with empirical distributions, that is, with the orderly arranging of data gathered from experience. But Chapter 6 in particular will also develop an important concept which has already appeared in our discussion—the concept of *expected value,* which is indispensable for our further progress.

Chapter 6

WHAT CAN
YOU EXPECT?

•

IF YOU BUY a ticket for a lottery, you have a good chance to win nothing, a small chance to win a little, and a very small chance to win a big prize. Add together the value of all the prizes, divide by the number of lottery tickets sold, and you get the fair price for a ticket. Anything you pay over that is a donation. In statistical language, this fair price is called the *expected value*. If we count in all the blanks as prizes with zero value, then the expected value of a lottery ticket is the sum of the prizes divided by their number. Probably no single prize has that exact value, but it is the return you will get per ticket if you buy up all the tickets, and in this sense it is a measure of what to "expect" as the return for one ticket.

This concept of expected value arose quite naturally in the days when probability theory was chiefly concerned with problems suggested by various forms of gambling. For example, how much is it worth to take a turn at a game, if the house will pay you one dollar to throw a six-sided die four times, without throwing a "6" once? Here it is a "success" to throw any number except the losing "6," and so the probability that you win against the house equals $(\frac{5}{6})^4 = .482$. (We might also say: the probability that an event will not occur in N trials equals q^N.) Therefore the break-even point for this game, and the expected value of a chance, is a little over 48 cents.

Insurance is also a kind of gamble which is based on statistical expectation, although here the expectations are best founded on experience rather than theory. In 1692, the British government raised £1,000,000 by selling life annuities. In those days, life was very uncertain, and the general feeling was that Death picked his victims at random, without regard to age or station. For every £100, the government promised to pay an annuity of £14 until death, regardless of the age of the annuitant. The government ultimately lost a pretty penny on that venture. In the very next year, Edmund Halley (of Halley's comet) used birth and death records of the city of Breslau, Germany, to prepare the first life expectancy tables, which showed how much more a child may expect of life than a youth, and how much more a youth may expect than an old man.

The flight insurance which you can purchase in any airport, before boarding your plane, has an expected value which is easier to calculate, at least in principle. For $.25, a vending machine will dispense a $10,000 insurance policy. The odds offered are 40,000 to 1, but of course this includes some allowance for overhead and profit. If the proportion of air disasters to safe flights is as 1 to 50,000, then the expected value of a $10,000 policy is $.20. The calculation assumes a universe of statistical passengers, all insured. Just as it is possible to talk about the expected value of the policy, it is also possible to talk about the expected survival of the passengers. Statistically speaking, each of those hypothetical passengers is 1/50,000th dead.

The expected value refers to the probable outcome of sampling in a specified universe. Sometimes, as in a gambling game, we know enough about the universe so that we can calculate the expected value as a matter of theory. More often, as with insurance, we must go by experience. Usually the arithmetic mean of a sample is the best estimate we have of the expected value in the universe from which the sample is taken. The arithmetic mean is a form of average with which you are doubtless already familiar. The most direct way to find it is to do with the scores (that is, the numerical values in the sample) as we did with the lottery prizes: add them and divide by their number. These operations are stated in the following formula:

$$\overline{X} = \frac{\Sigma \{X_i\}}{n} \cdot$$

We use $\overline{X}$ (read: X-*bar*) to stand for the arithmetic mean. When applied to a universe, it stands for the expected value, because that is the arithmetic mean of a universe. The subscript i is used to indicate an *individual* score, and the small n represents the number of scores in the sample. The capital Greek sigma, Σ, is a symbol which does not stand for a quantity, like X or n, and does not designate a particular kind of quantity, like the subscript i, but designates an operation. You are already familiar with a number of other operator symbols. For example, the line which separates numerator and denominator is such a symbol, which says "divide." Large Σ says: "sum of." Thus the formula repeats what we have already said in words: the arithmetic mean is the sum of all the individual scores, divided by n, which is their number and which is not to be confused with large N, which is the number of opportunities for an event to happen.

Sometimes it is convenient, before adding the scores, to set up a table of possible scores and tally how many there are of each kind. These are called class scores, and once this has been done, one can find the mean by taking the product of each class score and its frequency and dividing by n. This formula requires two new symbols: the subscript c, to designate a class score, and f, or frequency, to designate the number of scores in a class:

$$\overline{X} = \frac{\Sigma \, (fX_c)}{n}.$$

For example, the mean number of odd digits in 320 groups of 5 digits each, recorded in Table 3-1, is found in this way:

X_c	f	fX_c	
5	11	55	
4	49	196	
3	112	336	$\overline{X} = 815/320$
2	91	182	$\overline{X} = 2.547$
1	48	48	
0	11	0	
	320	815	

It does not really matter whether dividing by n takes place before or after the summation of products. If we divide first, the frequencies are changed into proportions. Therefore another way to obtain the expected value, or mean, is this:

$$\overline{X} = \Sigma \, (P_c \cdot X_c).$$

For example, the mean number of boys in a family of 5 (see Table 4-4) equals 5 (.036) + 4 (.170) + 3 (.321) + 2 (.303) + 1 (.143) = 2.572. (We shall see in a moment that this result includes a small error due to rounding of the class proportions.)

Finally, in a binomial distribution,

$$\overline{X} = Np.$$

Hence, the same result can be obtained more quickly, and with greater accuracy, by taking $\overline{X} = 5\,(.514) = 2.57$. It is not difficult to see why this formula works. Since p is the proportion of successes in the universe of simple events, it is also the proportion of successes mixed through the compound events (like the proportion of gravel mixed through a batch of concrete), and the various scores are simply counts of such successes. With N simple events forming each of the compound events, the expected value is N times that proportion.

REPRESENTATIVE SCORES

As stated above, we often use the mean of an empirical distribution to estimate the expected value of the universe or population from which the sample was taken. In other words, the mean is a representative score not only for the sample, but also for the whole population out of which the sample has been taken. If samples did not provide us with valid representative scores for populations, we would not be able to rely on experiments to give us useful information.

For scientific purposes, the use of a single score to represent a great many scores is often justified by the concept that each individual observation includes some error, but that these errors tend to cancel each other out when a suitable average is used. However, the concept of a representative score goes beyond this. It asserts that for many purposes it is possible to replace all the individual scores by a single representative score and accurately predict their total or cumulative effect.

It was no accident that the first table of life expectancies, which represented a practical application of this principle, was prepared by an astronomer. To astronomers, the concept of the mean as a working value has long been familiar. In 1619, Kepler had related the period which a planet took to encircle the sun to its mean distance from that body. Astronomers were also accustomed to the idea that for many purposes it was not necessary to take account of the varying speeds of the planets in different portions of their orbits; one could use the mean speed instead.

A similar use of the mean as a representative score exists, for example, when the amount of work that can be performed by a piston engine is calculated on the basis of the mean effective pressure on the piston, although the actual pressure which drives the piston undergoes great variations between the beginning and the end of the piston's stroke.

The most striking applications of this general method are in statistical mechanics. This is the branch of modern physics which determines the characteristics of a mass by means of a statistical analysis of the behavior of the molecules or other particles which compose it. Knowing the number and size of the particles, it is possible to calculate the mean free path, that is, the average distance which a particle can be expected to travel between collisions. Similar concepts are mean velocity and mean free time, which is the average time between molecular collisions. Many useful predictions can be made by taking mean values such as these as representative of all the particles, because the total effect of all the molecular activity is the same as it would be if all the molecules behaved in this representative manner.

The mean can be used in this way because of an interesting mathematical quality, namely, that in any distribution the sum of *deviations* is equal to zero. By deviation, we mean the algebraic difference between each score and the mean. The small letter x is used to stand for a deviation, and it is defined by this equation:

$$x_i = X_i - \overline{X}.$$

For example, suppose a distribution includes just three scores: 5, 9, and 19. The mean of these scores is 11, and the deviations are, respectively, -6, -2, and $+8$. In a symmetrical distribution, each positive deviation is balanced by an equal negative deviation, and it is obvious that the sum of deviations must be zero. When a distribution is not symmetrical, positive and negative deviations can no longer be matched, and as a rule they will not be equally numerous. Nevertheless, the sum of the positive deviations from the mean will always be exactly equal to the sum of negative deviations, just as in this illustrative example.

A very simple formal proof of this statement is given in Appendix A. In terms of a physical analogy, this means that if the scores are regarded as measured distances along a balance rod, each one marking a point where an equal weight is suspended from the rod, then the mean is the point where the whole system of weights is in balance. In other words, finding the mean of a distribution, by any of the formulas previously given, is a process of finding that "point of balance" which may be called the center of gravity for the distribution.

It is this mathematical quality of the mean which the Belgian, Lambert Quetelet (1796–1874), the "father of statistics," had in mind when he declared that "the average man is in a nation what the center of gravity is in a body; it is by having that central point in view that we arrive at the apprehension of all the phenomena of equilibrium and motion."

Quetelet also was an astronomer by training and profession. Before him, the word "statistics" meant no more than systematic tabulation of births, deaths, and taxes—observations which were of interest to statesmen, but not to scientists. He showed that these humdrum tabulations became much more meaningful when they were interpreted with the principles of probability in mind, in much the same way that astronomers interpreted their hundreds of conflicting observations of the same celestial phenomenon. To illustrate the importance of the mean as an expected value, we shall take an example from Quetelet's own pioneering work.

TABLE 6-1. The nature of murders for a series of years, as reported by Quetelet, based on "reports of criminal justice in France."

	1826	1827	1828	1829	1830	1831
Gun and pistol	56	64	60	61	57	88
Saber, sword, etc.	15	7	8	7	12	30
Knife	39	40	34	46	44	34
Cudgels, cane, etc.	23	28	31	24	12	21
Stones	20	20	21	21	11	9
Cutting, stabbing, and bruising instruments	35	40	42	45	46	49
Strangulation	2	5	2	2	2	4
Precipitating and drowning	6	16	6	1	4	3
Kicks and blows	28	12	21	23	17	26
Fire	0	1	0	1	0	0
Unknown	17	1	2	0	2	2
TOTALS	241	234	227	231	207	266

Source: Lambert Quetelet, *Treatise on Man and the Development of his Faculties* (Edinburgh, 1842).

Table 6-1 gives comparative figures on the incidence of murders, as recorded in the records of French courts for a period of 6 years. There are two aspects of this table to which Quetelet particularly draws attention. One is the regularity in the total number of murders each year (or, in other tables, of thefts, robberies, suicides, and so on); the other is the consistency, from year to year, in the relative frequency with which murders are committed with certain kinds of implements. These statistical regularities are regarded by him as proof that society is just as much the author of these acts as is the individual criminal. Here are some scattered sentences which express his point of view:

In a given state of society, resting under the influence of certain causes, regular effects are produced, which oscillate, as it were, around a fixed point, without undergoing any sensible altera-

tions. . . . Sad condition of humanity! We might even predict
annually how many individuals will stain their hands with the
blood of their fellow-men, how many will be forgers, how many
will deal in poison, pretty nearly in the same way as we may
foretell the annual births and deaths.

Society includes within itself the germs of all the crimes committed, and at the same time the necessary facilities for their
development. It is the social state, in some measure, which
prepares these crimes, and the criminal is merely the instrument
to carry them out. Every social state presupposes, then, a certain number and a certain order of crimes, these being merely
the necessary consequences of its organisation.

Quetelet's "moral statistics" stirred the conscience of Europe, and they precipitated a new phase of the eternal debate
on free will and social responsibility. Certainly he proved at
the very least that social science is unthinkable without statistics and that in dealing with such statistics, the mean is an
expected value by which we must guide our thinking. In his
words:

We may, therefore, by the results of the past, estimate what will
be realized in the future. This possibility of assigning beforehand
the number of accused and condemned persons which any
country will present, must give rise to serious reflections, since
it concerns the fate of several thousand men, who are driven, as
it were, in an irresistible manner, towards the tribunals, and the
condemnations which await them.

Quetelet's method also aroused a storm of protest, which
has not yet subsided, that "there is no average man." It is obvious, of course, that there can be no man who is average in
all respects. Nor is anyone today likely to agree with Quetelet's
extraordinary opinion that "an individual who should comprise in himself (in his own person), at a given period, all the
qualities of the average man, would at the same time represent
all which is grand, beautiful, and excellent." We have all been
too much influenced by the more recent emphasis on individ-

ual differences and the virtues of the exceptional person. However, it was Quetelet himself who laid the foundation for study of individual differences and exceptional men, by emphasizing that each individual can be understood and appraised only as a member of a distribution and by reference to the average.

To illustrate this fact, we shall look at two groups of scores on the Army Alpha Test, an intelligence test which was used

TABLE 6-2. Army Alpha Test scores of infantry riflemen and officer trainees.

ALPHA SCORE	RIFLEMEN	OFFICER CANDIDATES
200–224	0	2
175–199	7	51
150–174	40	288
125–149	93	632
100–124	216	556
75– 99	350	343
50– 74	441	111
25– 49	379	27
0– 24	142	4
n	1668	2014
$\overline{X}$	70.9	120.8

Source: Adapted from R. M. Yerkes, "Psychological Examining in the United States Army," Memoirs of the National Academy of Sciences, 15 (1921), Table 384.

to classify military personnel in World War I. This was the first really large-scale application of modern psychological methods, and its success greatly enhanced the prestige of psychology as a science. Indeed, it was a convincing realization of Quetelet's prophecy that the mental qualities of men would some day be measured. Looking at the two series of frequencies in Table 6-2, it is possible to make certain generalizations about "the average infantryman" and "the average officer candidate." But it would be completely false to think of each

rifleman or each officer candidate in terms of such averages
and ridiculous to regard the respective averages as "ideals."
However, bearing in mind that the mean score for riflemen is
71 and that the mean for officer candidates is 121, it is possible to make such individual judgments as "This infantryman
should be sent to officer's training school," or "That officer
candidate should be sent back to the ranks."

Despite the great value of the mean as a representative
score, it does have certain rivals for this function. The *mode*
and the *median* are two kinds of average which are often
quite useful under certain special conditions. Chapter 7 will
discuss them.

Chapter 7

TALKING ABOUT TYPES

•

PROBABLY THE MOST natural way for an untrained person to select an average or representative score is to pick one measurement out of all those available, because it seems to be the most typical. Suppose an American girl has come home after studying for a year in France, and her girl friend asks her, "How tall are the French men?" She might answer, "Well, my friend Pierre was 5 feet 7 inches, and I think that is quite typical."

In giving this answer, she selects the height of one man as representative. Other Frenchmen are shorter or taller than Pierre, but he is remembered as typical and, at least in this sense, ideal. When a systematic procedure is used to select the most frequent class score as representative, this statistic is called the *mode*. I shall illustrate the method on the basis of a fuller report on the height of Frenchmen—one which is almost 150 years old and which gives the height of 10,000 young men called up for service in the French army. (See Table 7-1.) The unit of measurement in Table 7-1 is one which was standard in France before the metric system was adopted, and, if it seems odd, just bear in mind that the *pouce,* or thumb, is simply the equivalent of an English inch. Twelve *pouces* make 1 French *pied,* just as 12 inches make 1

The World of Probability

TABLE 7-1. The height of French army conscripts, as reported by Hargenvillier in 1817.

Height	Class Frequency	Cumulative Frequency
Above 65 thumbs*	249	10,000
64 to 65 "	319	9,751
63 to 64 "	553	9,432
62 to 63 "	878	8,879
61 to 62 "	1,141	8,001
60 to 61 "	1,441	6,860
59 to 60 "	1,399	5,419
58 to 59 "	1,158	4,020
Below 58 "	2,862	2,862
	10,000	

Source: Based on a table in Lambert Quetelet, *Treatise on Man and the Development of his Faculties* (Edinburgh, 1842).
* The *pouce,* or thumb, is an old French measure equal to 2.71 centimeters, or 1.07 inches.

English foot. However, the French *pied* was very nearly 13 English inches.

These data are faulty in the sense that the tallest men have been lumped together into one class at the upper end of the distribution, and the short men, including all those who were excused from military duty because of their short stature, are lumped into one class at the lower end of the distribution. There seem to be too many of these, which creates a suspicion that some succeeded in having their heights shaved a little for a fee. However, this circumstance does not make it impossible to select a representative score for the table.

The typical or most numerous class consists of young men whose height is between 60 and 61 thumbs. We can represent all these cases by the mid-value of the class, which is 60.5 thumbs, or about 5 feet 4 inches. This is called the *mode.* The entire procedure involves three steps: (1) group the possible measurements into a series of convenient classes; (2) record the frequency with which observations fall into each class; (3) select as typical the class score which has the highest frequency. (The category "below 58" cannot be regarded as one class, for a class must represent an equal interval on the dimension of measurement.)

The mode has serious limitations as a representative score for empirical data. In small samples it is a very uncertain value, and even in large samples it depends too much on just how the classes were selected. Sometimes it is not possible to determine "the" mode, because two or more classes may have the same frequency, and they may not even be adjacent classes. However, the mode is most useful just when it seems to make least sense as a representative score, because that is when it calls our attention to a kind of error which might otherwise be overlooked.

Most distributions, when they are based on a fairly large number of observations, are distinctly *unimodal,* that is, there is one class frequency which exceeds any other. Occasionally, however, it happens that a distribution is *bimodal.* This means that two classes of relatively high frequency are separated by one or more classes with lower frequency than either of them. Even though the frequencies in these two classes may be quite unequal, both should be called modal classes if they are separated by a region of distinctly lower frequency. Whenever this happens it deserves careful attention because it means that a strong nonchance influence is tending to separate the scores into two "types."

Figure 1 is an example of bimodality. It presents data on taste sensitivity of 855 persons for phenylthiocarbamide. This is a substance which tastes quite bitter to some people, but which others cannot taste even in concentrations 10,000 times stronger. Each column in the figure shows how many persons, in the sample studied, were just able to detect the bitter taste in a certain solution. Moving from left to right, each solution is half as strong as the one before it. The sharp bimodality

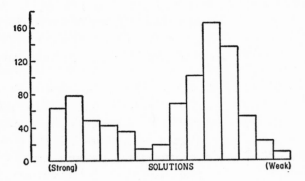

FIGURE 1. Taste thresholds of 855 persons for phenylthiocarbamide. From left to right each solution is half as strong as the one preceding. Based on H. Kalmus, "Inherited Sense Defects," *Scientific American,* 186 (1952), 64–70.

of this distribution shows that a single factor predominates in deciding whether an individual is a "taster" or a "nontaster," although other factors also influence the sensitivity. This points to a simple hereditary mechanism, and therefore this test has been used as a kind of tracer to study the genetic make-up of populations. The proportion of nontasters is relatively low among Chinese and Japanese and also among American Indians, which helps to confirm that America was first populated by migrants from northern Asia. The peoples of southeast Asia have a higher proportion of nontasters.

THE MEDIAN

Let us turn back to the data on the height of French army recruits, given in Table 7-1, which we have already used to illustrate the mode. There is another way to get a useful representative score from these data. Look at the column of cumulative frequencies in the table. If we were to divide all the men into two divisions, the "tall" and the "short," with 5,000 men in each division, the cutting point would fall somewhere in the "59 to 60" class. Of the 1,399 men in that class, 980 would be needed to make up the full 5,000 for the "short men's division," while 419 would go into the "tall men's division." Therefore the exact cutting point must lie close to $59 + (980/1399) = 59.7$. This value, which has just as many individual scores above it as below it, is called the *median*.

The median is a useful representative score whenever the extreme scores in the distribution are untrustworthy or when, for some other reason, we want to reduce their influence. In this case, we suspect that there has been some tampering with the lower values, and in any case, we are not given actual measurements for the tallest and the shortest individuals. This kind of situation is not unusual in research work, even when the data are gathered with great care. For example, if half a dozen monkeys are required to solve a mechanical puzzle, five of them may do it in from two to five minutes, and the last may still not succeed after an hour. In such a case, the median time is more representative than the mean, because it is not too much influenced by that extreme case.

The median is used regularly in certain kinds of medical research. To tell how powerful a poison is, the pharmacologist tries several dosages on different groups of animals and then estimates how strong the dose would have to be to kill half the animals to which it is administered. This median lethal dose is taken as representative for comparison with other poisons, or to study methods of providing protection against the poison. It would be much more difficult and perhaps even impossible to determine the mean dose which is needed to kill all, and even if it were possible to do so, this figure might be unduly influenced by just one or two animals which were especially resistant to the poison.

The median, rather than the mean, is the representative

score used to discuss incomes, or family size, or any other phenomenon for which there are a great many low scores and relatively few very high ones.

Finally, here is an unusual example of a research report in which the median is used along with the mean, and both together tell an interesting story. Physiologists today are able to place tiny electrodes into single nerve cells (neurons) of the brain, and record their activity. Each nerve cell is like a tiny electric battery, which keeps building up a charge and then discharging it, at a fairly constant rate under "resting" conditions, that is, when the animal is not responding to any outside stimulation. This activity goes on constantly, even during sleep, and the frequency of discharge is a good measure of a neuron's activity, because each discharge is always of the same intensity. In this experiment the spontaneous discharge rates of many individual cells were recorded, in different parts of the cat's brain, both while the animals were awake and while they were asleep. We shall consider only the mean and median rates of discharge under these two conditions for ninety nerve cells in one part of the brain. Results in other portions were similar.

As Table 7-2 shows, the mean rate of activity increases when the animal wakes up, but the median decreases. These results show that there are two different types of neurons in the brain—one set of neurons which increases their rate of discharge when the animal wakes up, and another more nu-

TABLE 7-2. Mean and median values, during sleep and waking, for rate of discharge of ninety neurons in the visual cortex of cat.

	MEAN	MEDIAN
While asleep	7.30	5.20
While awake	7.95	3.56

Source: E. V. Evarts, E. Bental, B. Bihari, and P. R. Huttenlocher, "Spontaneous Discharge of Single Neurons during Sleep and Waking," *Science,* 135 (1962), 726–728.

merous set which decreases the rate of discharge, so that the median rate actually declines. This finding is in line with a whole new approach to the understanding of the brain and nervous system, which emphasizes that nerve cells do not all do the same kind of work, as we used to believe, but are specialized for different activities.

Chapter 8

VARIATIONS ON
A CHANCE THEME

•

WE TURN BACK to the study of probability distributions.

In Chapter 4, we saw that the probability of a compound event which combines X successes and $N - X$ failures, in N opportunities, can be stated as the product of three factors:

(1) the number of ways there are to succeed X times in N trials, which is $\binom{N}{X}$;

(2) The X-fold product of the probability of each success; and

(3) the $(N - X)$-fold product of the probability of each failure.

Stated as a formula:

$$P\{X\} = \binom{N}{X} p^X q^{N-X}.$$

Otherwise stated, this calculation consists in taking all the possible products in which p and q appear, together, N times. That is the same calculation which is needed to raise the binomial, $p + q$, to the Nth power. Therefore any distribution of this kind is called binomial.

The leap-frog pattern of p's and q's in a binomial distribution can be simplified in some cases and camouflaged in others to provide convenient solutions for a great variety of problems. This chapter will deal with three variations on this pattern of chance. Others, even more important, will appear in later chapters. But we shall find that all probability distributions are essentially variations on the binomial pattern. Understanding the binomial distribution is the key to understanding them all.

As our first variation, just for warming up, let us consider the type of situation which is governed by that ancient adage, "If at first you don't succeed, try, try again." We need only one success, but we do not know how many attempts may be necessary to achieve it. Digging for an oil well in an untried field, where the geological conditions may be taken to indicate a certain probability for discovery, is a matter of this sort. Or, if your interest runs to archaeology rather than oil, exploring dunes in a Mesopotamian desert in the hope of finding the remains of an ancient village illustrates this.

Let us assume that the chance of success in each dig is 1 in 10. We have enough capital to finance ten tries, and if it should turn out that all are dry holes, we will be bankrupt of cash and reputation. What is the chance for fame and/or fortune?

For this problem $N = 10$, $p = .1$, $q = .9$. If we let $X = 1$ and substitute these values into the formula of the binomial distribution, we find the probability for just 1 success in 10 tries:

$$P\{1\} = \binom{10}{1} (.1)(.9)^9 = .387.$$

But the chance for success in our venture is really better than that, because this calculation does not include combinations of more than 1 success in 10 tries. What we must do to solve our problem is to keep X equal to 1, but let N change. For each value of N, we must find the probability that the last trial, and only the last, will be a success, following $N - 1$ failures. By the multiplication rule, this probability equals $q^{N-1}p$.

As in any probability distribution, the sum of these products will add up to 1 if all the possibilities are taken into account, that is, if N is allowed to take all positive integral values. This implies that even for a large number of attempts, there is always a slight possibility that success will elude us. The chance of just 1 success in 10 tries is the sum of these products for values of N from 1 to 10, inclusive.

TABLE 8-1. A geometric probability distribution: the chance of a first success on each of ten trials, together with the cumulative probability of success, if $p = .10$.

N	pq^{N-1}	P_{cum}	N	pq^{N-1}	P_{cum}
1	.1000	.1000	6	.0590	.4685
2	.0900	.1900	7	.0531	.5216
3	.0810	.2710	8	.0478	.5694
4	.0729	.3439	9	.0430	.6124
5	.0656	.4095	10	.0387	.6511

Table 8-1 shows the calculation for this problem. We do not have as much as a 50:50 chance unless we are ready to undertake at least seven tries, and even with ten tries the chance of success is not quite $\frac{2}{3}$. This is one of those cases where the calculated probability does not agree with the intuitive answer which most people would give. A probability distribution of this kind is called *geometric,* because the probability declines in a steady proportion from one step to the next. This decline does not mean that the chance of success is any less for the tenth dig, per se, than for the first dig, but neither do we have any better chance for success on the tenth dig, because we have failed nine times before. Trial by trial, the probability of success remains the same, just as the chance for a head remains the same every time you flip a coin into the air, no matter what may have been the results for all the spins that went before. But the conditional probability of a first success on any given trial, following a certain number of failures, does not remain the same. It is less likely that we will have our *first* success on the tenth trial rather than on the ninth, because there is more likelihood that we shall have had at least one success in nine trials than in eight.

Notice that in this problem the cumulative probability after N trials can be obtained as the difference between 1 and the probability of no successes whatever during the same number of trials. For $N = 10$, this gives us

$$P\{1\} = 1 - .9^{10} = 1 - .3489 = .6511.$$

Here is another application. It has been conjectured that in this period of cold war, in which the strategic air defense has had several false alerts, there is possibly 1 chance in 100 that a nuclear war might be precipitated "inadvertently," during any given year, without either adversary intending to start such a war or even one of the old-fashioned kind. Taking this probability as correct, there is about a 22 per cent probability that this tragic event will occur in a period of twenty-five years. ($P = 1 - .99^{25} = .222$.)

NEGATIVE BINOMIAL DISTRIBUTIONS

As our second variation, let us consider the probability of attaining a fixed number of successes within a certain number of trials. For example, a tennis match must be won by 2 sets out of 3, a World Series by 4 games out of 7. The problem stipulates a necessary number of successes (that is, X has a fixed value), but it permits the number of failures, Y, to vary up to some maximum, which in these examples equals $X - 1$, but need not necessarily have that value.

We must compute the probability separately for each permissible value of Y. In each case, we take the probability that Y failures and X – 1 successes will occur together in a series of X + Y – 1 trials, in any order, and multiply this by the probability that the next and final trial will be a success. This conditional probability equals

$$\binom{X + Y - 1}{Y} p^X q^Y.$$

This formula gives rise to the *negative binomial* distribution. It has many interesting applications. Let us first take one that is mildly entertaining.

In 1963, when the Dodgers were about to meet the Yankees in the World Series, pre-series betting favored the Yankees. It seemed a fair overall estimate that the probability of a Dodger victory in any one game equaled .45. What chance did they have to win the series? Here X = 4, and Y takes all the values from 0 to 3, inclusive. The calculation is shown in Table 8-2. It shows that the Dodgers had about 4 chances in

TABLE 8-2. A negative binomial distribution: the probability of winning four games before losing four, if the probability of each win equals .45. Number of games lost equals Y.

Y	$\binom{Y + 3}{Y}$	$.45^4$	$.55^Y$	$P\{Y\}$
0	1	.041	1.	.041
1	4	.041	.55	.090
2	10	.041	.303	.124
3	20	.041	.166	.136
				.391

10 to win and about 1 chance in 25 to sweep the series. Most readers will remember that this improbable outcome did come

to pass. The event does not prove that the initial assumptions were faulty. After all, even things that happen "only once in 100 times" by chance will happen by chance—once in 100 times.

Here is a less sporting application, for which the calculation appears in Table 8-3. How many bombers must be sent

TABLE 8-3. A negative binomial distribution: the probability of scoring three bomb hits, when the probability of each single hit equals .3. The number of bombers which fail to hit the target equals Y.

Y	$\binom{Y+2}{Y}$	$.3^3$	$.7^Y$	$P\{Y\}$	P_{cum}
0	1	.027	1.	.027	.027
1	3	.027	.700	.057	.084
2	6	.027	.490	.079	.163
3	10	.027	.343	.093	.256
4	15	.027	.240	.097	.353
5	21	.027	.168	.095	.448
6	28	.027	.118	.089	.537
7	36	.027	.083	.080	.617
8	45	.027	.058	.070	.687
9	55	.027	.041	.060	.747
10	66	.027	.028	.050	.797
11	78	.027	.020	.042	.839
12	91	.027	.014	.034	.873
13	105	.027	.010	.027	.900

over a target area, if the probability of a hit by each bomber is .3, and headquarters demands a 90 per cent probability that at least three hits will be scored? Since Y represents the number of bombers which fail to hit the target, the mission must be carried out by Y + 3 bombers. Sixteen bombers must go on the raid to make the cumulative probability reach the desired level.

THE POISSON DISTRIBUTION

Our third variation on the binomial distribution is one which is used to calculate the probability distribution for an event which has an extremely small probability, but which nevertheless occurs a good many times, because there are so very many opportunities for it to happen. Accidents are of that sort. They are often so extraordinary that we hear the excuse, "It was just one chance in a million." Nevertheless, they keep happening with impressive regularity. Very small probabilities, which add up to very large totals, are also characteristic of collisions between molecules, of the spread of contagious diseases, and of the number of drunken-driving arrests among Sunday drivers. As you deduce from these examples, *p* in these problems is more often the probability of a disaster than the probability of a success.

In all such cases, it is quite impractical, and often humanly impossible, to calculate probabilities in the way that we have been doing up to now. So far, we have always used some stipulated value of *N*, which is the number of opportunities for the event to happen. In other words, we have been dealing with each problem in a finite universe. When *N* is very large, this method would require patience and industry in the tremendous amounts found only in high-speed electronic computers, not in humans. But by sleight of hand the mathematician can eliminate *N* from the calculations, and in its place we find the almost magical ratio *e*, the so-called natural base of logarithms.

This remarkable ratio is needed in every calculation which involves a constant rate of growth or shrinkage. Suppose, for example, that a colony of bacteria is multiplying at a constant rate. Count the bacteria on the hour and again ten minutes later. Determine exactly how long it would take for the colony to double its numbers if it were to increase by the same amount (not the same rate, or percentage) every ten minutes. If this total period is long enough so that ten minutes is a very small fraction of it, then at the end of the period the colony, growing at a constant rate, will have multiplied approximately 2.718 times. This is the ratio e. It is a limit, a maximum ratio which would be attained under these conditions if the ten-minute period is only an infinitesimal fraction of the period which would be required for doubling by constant increments. However, it gives a surprisingly good approximation to the result in many realistic situations. If, for example, the actual time required is eight hours, or 48 periods of ten minutes each, then by growing at a constant rate the colony will actually multiply only about 2.70 times in the same period of time. Under these conditions, the value of e is an estimate which is in error by about 1 per cent.

In probability theory we are interested not in growth but in shrinkage, or negative growth: that is, not in e, but in its reciprocal, $1/e$, which equals approximately .368. A short discussion of shrinkage in ordinary and extraordinary garments will prepare us to understand the part that $1/e$ plays in the calculation of probabilities.

Suppose you buy a shirt which carries the strange guarantee that it will shrink exactly 1 per cent in every wash. This is not very promising from the standpoint of comfortable fit, but neither does it mean that if you wash it 100 times, the shirt will shrink 100 per cent—that is, to nothing at all. The amount of shrinkage will be less from one wash to the next, although the rate of shrinkage is constant. How big will the shirt be after 100 washes, compared to its original size? The answer is $.99^{100}$, which equals .366.

Compare this with the effect of 20 washes on a garment which shrinks 5 per cent in each wash or of 1,000 washes on a garment which shrinks 0.1 per cent each time. In the first case, we have $.95^{20}$, which is .358; in the second, we have

$.999^{1000}$, which is .3677. There is surprisingly little spread among these values, and, in fact, they are approaching a limiting value, $1/e$, which is in the neighborhood of .3679. With constant shrinkage under these conditions, no shirt can shrink below this limit. If the angel Gabriel wears a robe which he washes every day throughout all eternity, and if the rate of shrinkage on each wash is equal to the proportionate length of one day to eternity, then at the end of time it will have shrunk to .36788 of its original size. We need not doubt that the angels know these facts and make sufficient allowance for them in the initial cut of their flowing robes, because it is good mathematical gospel that the magic of e is woven into all created things.

Shrinkage enters into the calculation of probabilities in the following manner. In the binomial distribution, the probability of a zero score equals q^N. Now, take any binomial distribution which has an expected value equal to 1. This means that $Np = 1$, just as, in each of our shrinkage problems, the rate of shrinkage multiplied by the number of washes equaled 1. Whenever this condition is satisfied, q^N will be approximately equal to $1/e$. The approximation will be increasingly exact as the value of N increases. This in turn implies that the value of p becomes smaller, because we must not disturb the relationship $Np = 1$.

Here we have an important breakthrough in learning how to calculate probabilities in a very large universe. No matter what the value of N may be, provided only that it be a large number, the probability of a zero score equals $1/e$. To illustrate: if in a certain small city there are six traffic fatalities in an average year, the expected number each month is ½. Since there are thousands of opportunities for accidents, it is evident that p is a very small proportion. Two months is the period in which 1 accident is to be expected, on the average. Therefore the probability that a period of two months will pass without any traffic fatalities equals $1/e$, or .368. When N is not large, this method will still give a fairly good approximation. In the problem on Page 67, we assumed that the chance for a successful dig is 1 in 10. We found that the chance for no successes in 10 trials equals .349. A hasty approximation would be $1/e$, which is .368.

It is not difficult to apply this principle, along with the multiplication law, in order to calculate the probability for zero occurrences when the expected score is either greater or less than 1. The probability that four months will pass without a traffic fatality becomes $.368^2 = .135$. The probability that one month will pass without a fatal accident equals $.368^{1/2} = .607$. In general, if $\overline{X}$ is the expected score, the probability of a zero score may be stated thus:

$$P\{0\} = (1/e)^{\overline{X}}.$$

The probability that this city might go through a whole year without a fatal traffic accident equals $(1/e)^6$, which is approximately .0025.

TABLE 8-4. Values of $(1/e)^{\overline{X}}$. For values of $\overline{X}$ which do not appear in the table, use the relationship $(1/e)^{A+B} = (1/e)^A (1/e)^B$. For example, $(1/e)^{3.4} = (.0498)(.670) = .0334$.

$\overline{X}$	$(1/e)^{\overline{X}}$	$\overline{X}$	$(1/e)^{\overline{X}}$	$\overline{X}$	$(1/e)^{\overline{X}}$
.01	.990	0.1	.905	1.0	.368
.02	.980	0.2	.819	2.0	.135
.03	.970	0.3	.741	3.0	.0498
.04	.961	0.4	.670	4.0	.0183
.05	.951	0.5	.607	5.0	.00674
.06	.942	0.6	.549	6.0	.00248
.07	.932	0.7	.497	7.0	.00091
.08	.923	0.8	.449	8.0	.00034
.09	.914	0.9	.407	9.0	.00012

Table 8-4 gives the values of this function. (In Chapter 10, we will see that the same table can also be used to find probabilities in what is called the *normal distribution*.)

Once we know how to find the probability of a zero score, we have a firm base from which to calculate other probabilities. In Chapter 4 we saw that in any binomial distribution,

$$P\{X\} = \frac{p}{q} \cdot \frac{N - X + 1}{X} P\{X - 1\}.$$

Let us restate this in the following form:

$$P\{X\} = \frac{pN - pX + p}{qX} P\{X - 1\}.$$

When p is a very small proportion and N is a very large number, $pX + p$ is a negligible quantity. In that case, we can also ignore q, because it is very nearly 1. Finally, since $pN = \overline{X}$, we are left with this:

$$P\{X\} = \frac{\overline{X}}{X} P\{X - 1\}.$$

That is, once we know the probability of any score, to find the probability of the next higher score it is only necessary to divide by X, and multiply by $\overline{X}$. In the example we have been using, this gives:

$$P\{0\} = (1/e)^6 \qquad = .00248$$
$$P\{1\} = (6/1)\,P\{0\} = .01488$$
$$P\{2\} = (6/2)\,P\{1\} = .04464, \text{ etc.}$$

The complete probability distribution is given in Table 8-5. This is called *Poisson's distribution*. Siméon Denis Poisson

(1781–1840) was a versatile mathematical physicist who made important contributions to the theory of heat, capillary action, hydrostatic préssure, and elasticity. However, the contribution which now holds our attention was presented in a treatise dealing with the probability of verdicts in criminal trials. Three-fourths of a century went by before Rutherford

TABLE 8-5. A Poisson probability distribution: the probability of various numbers of traffic fatalities per annum in a city in which six such accidents are "expected" each year.

X	P {X}	X	P {X}	X	P {X}
0	.002	6	.161	11	.023
1	.015	7	.138	12	.011
2	.045	8	.103	13	.005
3	.089	9	.069	14	.002
4	.134	10	.041	15	.001
5	.161				
					1.000

and Geiger, in their pioneering study of alpha radiation, showed that it could have important scientific applications. Since then, it has found countless uses in many fields of science and technology. Telephone engineers use it to calculate the volume of traffic on trunk lines and switchboards, which explains why the most extensive tables of the Poisson distribution are found in a publication of the Bell Laboratories.

Cosmic rays, wars per century, the kicks of army mules, resignations by Supreme Court justices, the number of wormy apples in a barrel—there seems no end to the applications of the Poisson distribution. The following example is taken from an investigation of mitosis—the splitting of the nucleus in a living cell just before the cell divides. The authors explain that, when samples of tissue are examined under the microscope, it often seems that cells which are undergoing mitosis tend to

The World of Probability

occur in clusters rather than just being randomly scattered. If this is really so, it means that some influence in the neighborhood of these cells is encouraging the mitosis, rather than that the internal condition of the cell itself determines when it shall divide. (As you know, any bit of new knowledge about the conditions which favor cell division may be a key to unlock the riddle of cancer.)

To investigate this question, they prepared five samples of skin, taken from the ears of adult mice. They studied each sample under the miscroscope, through an optical grid which marked off one hundred equal shares, each containing about

TABLE 8-6. An application of the Poisson distribution: frequencies of mitoses observed (f_o) and expected (f_e) in 100 grid squares, in microscopic examination of epithelial tissue from the ear of an adult mouse.

The "test of good fit" which is performed in the last column will be discussed in Chapter 13.

MITOSES	f_o	f_e	$(f_o - f_e)^2 / f_e$
0	1	1.5	.42
1	5	6.3	
2	16	13.2	.59
3	17	18.5	.12
4	26	19.4	2.24
5	11	16.3	1.72
6	9	11.4	.51
7	9	6.9	.64
8	2	3.6	
9	1	1.7	
10	2	0.7	0.1
11	1	0.3	
12	0	0.0	
	100	99.8	6.25

Source: J. V. Frei, W. O'N. Waugh, and A. C. Ritchie, "Mitoses: Distribution in Mouse Ear Epidermis," *Science*, 140 (1963), 487–488, p. 488.

700 to 800 cells. In one sample, which we shall use for our example, they counted 420 mitoses. (See the column of observed frequencies in Table 8-6.) This means that the probability of a mitotic cell is approximately 420/75,000 or .0056. But we do not need to pay any attention to this value. The calculation of the Poisson distribution starts with the fact that the expected number of mitoses is 4.2 for each unit of the optical grid. Therefore the probability that a given unit will contain no mitoses equals $(1/e)^{4.2}$. Using Table 8-4, we find that $(1/e)^{4.2} = (.0183)\ (.819) = .015$. The other probabilities are calculated from this base, in the way we have already shown.

Since there are 100 grid units, multiplying by 100 will change the probabilities into expected or theoretical frequencies. We should expect to find no mitoses in 1.5 per cent of the grid squares, one mitosis in 6.3 per cent, and so forth. When we compare these values with the observed frequencies, there seems no reason to suppose that mitoses occur in clusters. On the contrary, the observed distribution seems to fit the theoretical chance distribution rather well. Therefore the experiment supports the interpretation that cell mitoses, at least in healthy tissue, are determined solely by conditions inside the cells and are not influenced by conditions outside the cells in their immediate neighborhood.

The Poisson distribution shows the effect of pushing luck to the limit, in the sense of making p (which is here more often the probability of a disaster than of a success) immeasurably small. In Chapter 10 we will investigate the effect of pushing opportunity to the limit, that is, we shall let p be undiminished, but we shall nevertheless make the value of N immeasurably large. This assumption will give rise to the very important distribution which is variously called the Gaussian curve, the normal curve, and the law of error. However, the formula for that distribution requires that we shall stop thinking of scores as separate quantities, but rather in terms of their relationships to one another and to the distribution as a whole. Instead of talking about "scores," which are like distances measured out along a straight line, we must begin to talk about "squares." Chapter 9 will reveal some of the advantages obtained by this device and will prepare us for a great deal of what is to follow.

Chapter 9

WHY BE INTERESTED
IN SQUARES?

●

Riddle: In what way does a debater's speech resemble the performance of a marksman? *Answer:* In both cases, it is important to concentrate on the central point. The debater wins no points for talking all around his subject, and the marksman wins no medals because his hits surround the bull's eye on all sides. Scatter-brained and scatter-aimed are just two kinds of error.

It is easy to see that scatter is an important aspect of any score distribution. A drug that causes a normal adult to grow drowsy and fall asleep in a time between 20 and 30 minutes after it is taken is much more useful than one that produces the same effect anywhere between 5 and 45 minutes after taking. The fact that they both take effect in 25 minutes "on the average" does not make them equivalent.

Differences in scatter can be expressed (as in this example) by comparing the *range* of scores in one distribution with that in another. The range is the difference between the highest and lowest score.

In a manufacturing plant, the quality control engineer is supposed to see that the product meets specifications. To do his job, he pays less attention to the precise measurements of the parts being produced than to the amount of scatter in those measurements, as shown by their range in small samples. If the inspectors were required to make measurements on every finished part, a corps of them might be needed for every lathe or press. What they actually do is to take small random samples, say five items out of each batch of one hundred, and report the range for each sample. When the measurements start to become inconsistent, even though they are still within the specified tolerance limits, it is a sign that something is starting to go wrong on the production line. In this way trouble is detected before it develops too far—a result which justifies calling the process one of *quality control* rather than just *inspection*. The range is useful in work like this because it takes virtually no time at all to calculate it in a small sample, and the job can be done with very little training.

The sales department will use a different statistic of scatter to describe the amount of variation which can be expected in the finished product. For example, the expected useful life of a TV picture tube might be stated by giving the median life and the mid-quartile range—which means that one-fourth of the tubes will fall below the lower limit of the range, and one-fourth will be above the upper limit.

For many years, scientists used to report the amount of variability in their results by calculating an *average* (or mean) *deviation*. You will recall from Chapter 6 that in any distribution the sum of deviations equals zero, and therefore if an average deviation is to have any meaning, it must be based on the sum of absolute deviations, that is, deviations taken simply according to size, without regard to plus or minus signs. This statistic offers useful information in a form which is readily understood by any intelligent reader. It is widely used in reports intended to be read by laymen, because it takes no special training to grasp the significance of a statement, for example, that although two cities have the same annual rainfall of 24 inches, the average deviation in one city is 3 inches, and in the other, 6 inches. However, in scientific work the average deviation has fallen out of use.

The most useful measures of scatter are based not on differences in raw scores, nor even on deviation scores, but on squared deviation scores. This requires more work, but the results are worth it.

We often refer to a sum of squared deviation scores simply as "the sum of squares." By definition,

$$\Sigma x^2 = \Sigma \ (X_i - \overline{X})^2.$$

This calls for taking the difference between each score and the mean of the distribution, squaring the difference, and then adding all the squares together. You will see later that there is a much more economical way to obtain the same result. But why do we want it at all? Why should we think that when a score is twice as far from the mean, it should be given, for some purposes at least, four times the weight, instead of just twice, as on a seesaw balance?

It is difficult to explain in advance what the advantage is in using squares rather than ordinary or "linear" scores. Do not let anyone tell you (although you will read it in some books) that we do this to get rid of the minus signs on some of the deviations. There is nothing wrong with adding deviations as absolute magnitudes, without regard to their algebraic signs. It happens, however, that for purposes of analysis the sum of absolute deviations is much less useful than the sum of their squares. We use the sum of squares because it gives results and not because of any fastidious preference for removing algebraic signs by a complicated procedure instead of a simple one.

You can detect a hint of magic in the fact that in any binomial distribution, the mean square equals Npq. That is, it is equal to the mean number of successes in N opportunities, multiplied by the probability of failure. In a Poisson distribution, where the probability of failure approaches unity, the mean square equals the expected value, $\overline{X}$. We shall prove these facts later (in Appendix D). They play a necessary part in the formula for the normal distribution, the so-called law of error, which we shall discuss at length in Chapter 10. We mention them now only as tending to show that the mean square is related to fundamental characteristics of probability distributions.

The sum of squares provides us with a measure of the strength of chance influences needed to produce a certain amount of scatter. Let us illustrate this statement by a discussion of Brownian movement. This is the unpredictable microscopic motion of tiny particles suspended in a liquid. (You see something of the same sort, on a larger scale, when you watch motes of dust dancing in a beam of sunlight.) The motion receives its name from the fact that it was first described by Robert Brown, a botanist, in 1827. Brown's observations were on fine grains of pollen, and at first he thought that these seemingly spontaneous movements might be an expression of life, but he decided they were of a mechanical nature. Several decades later, after heat had been explained as an effect of molecular motion, it became possible to understand the real nature of Brownian movement, and in time the precise study of this phenomenon became an important source of verification for theories of molecular physics.

By now it is certain that Brownian movement is the result of random buffeting of small particles by surrounding molecules. The same phenomenon is responsible for diffusion of a substance which is allowed to dissolve slowly, without stirring, in a glass of water. We shall consider only the gross movement of each particle, that is, the net displacement from its position at the start of observations. The smaller the particle, the more erratic will its movements seem, because impacts from different directions balance out less effectively on a small surface than on a large one. The net displacement is a result of many small movements in various directions, and of course this tends to increase with time, but not in direct proportion to it. A particle which is first pushed in one direction will later by chance be pushed in another direction, perhaps even back toward the starting point. If, for many particles, one measures the displacement over a given period of time, one can verify what Einstein predicted by a statistical analysis: that the sum of the squared displacements—and hence also the mean square—increases in proportion to the time. Let us consider why this should be so.

If the temperature and other essential conditions remain the same, time is a direct measure of the forces responsible for the movement. In twice as much time, each particle has twice as much exposure to the random action of bombarding molecules. But doubling the time does not produce double the movement, measured as straight-line distance from start to finish. To double this distance, one needs on the average four times as much exposure to the same chance forces. It is the square of the net displacement which measures exposure to chance.

This is because chance forces are not focused on a goal; they are not directed toward pushing the particle in a given direction. They are exerted in all directions, just as a light which is not focused spreads through space in all directions until it meets an obstacle. To appear equally bright at double the distance, a light must be four times as strong at the origin, because at that distance the same amount of light is spread over four times as much area. In the same way, it will take four times as much undirected, random molecular bombardment to produce, on the average, twice as much displacement, because we cannot expect that the particle will be pushed along steadily in the same direction.

Karl Przibram showed that Einstein's rule for Brownian movement also holds for the movements of paramoecia. Under low-power magnification, these little organisms, which are just large enough to be detected as white specks by the naked eye, can be seen to move erratically in a drop of water. There is a cause behind each twist and turn, but in our perspective its wanderings are random and indeterminate, like Brownian movement, and the sum of squares of the displacements is proportional to the elapsed time.

In any set of scores, each individual score is analogous to the net displacement of a Brownian particle. The mean of the distribution can be regarded as the common starting point. The impact of many chance influences produces a net displacement, that is, a deviation score. This is different for each individual case, as it is for each particle suspended in a liquid, but the mean squared deviation provides a valid estimate of the strength of the chance influences which are present in the situation.

Brownian movement is a kind of pure error, because it is entirely due to chance effects. But imagine a swarm of toy balloons released high in the sky with no strings attached. Partly they move like Brownian particles, as they rise and dip and move every-which-way under the influence of random currents of air. But partly they move together in the direction of the prevailing wind, however slight. As they move they tend to get farther apart, because the crosswinds are not precisely the same everywhere and at every instant. If we have some suitable ground point for reference, we can measure the prevailing wind by the general movement of the balloons, and we can also measure its variability by the extent of scattering. In the movement of each balloon, the Brownian-like effects, which are due to innumerable chance influences, are added to the main effect due to the prevailing wind. The same thing is true of any set of objects which are exposed to an experimental treatment plus chance influences. By studying variability among the scores, we can draw conclusions about the relative importance of chance and the experimental treatment.

In the remainder of this chapter, we want to see how the sum of squares for a set of experimental scores can be analyzed to reveal the action of nonchance influences—prevailing winds, as it were—and to provide a measure of their intensity. As an illustration we shall select a fascinating little experiment, in which the behavior of flatworms upsets some widely accepted ideas about the nature of memory.

ON THE EDUCATION OF WORMS

Most people believe that we learn only with our brains, that everything we learn is stored in our brains, and that the same must hold true for all animals that are capable of learning. These assumptions are far from certain. About fifty years ago, R. M. Yerkes demonstrated that the earthworm can learn a simple maze. This was not too surprising in itself, because the earthworm does possess a primitive brain. But then he chopped off the first few segments of one worm and gave it time to regenerate a new "head" and a new brain. When it was put back into the maze, the worm still showed some effects of its previous training. The flatworm is even more primitive than the earthworm, but its nervous system resembles that of the earthworm—and of man—in two important repects: (1) it has a "brain"—a special concentration of nervous tissue at the front end of the nervous system, which regulates a good deal of the animal's behavior, including the pattern of locomotion—and (2) it is the lowliest creature which has a synaptic nervous system. This means in essence that the process of communication within the nervous system depends on the action of "chemical messengers" which are released into tiny gaps, or synapses, between the nerve cells. Perhaps for these reasons the flatworm can learn.

We ordinarily place an exaggerated value on learning as a way to solve life's problems. It is true that man could not get

88 *The World of Probability*

along without it, but many animals can, and the fact that a worm can learn has nothing to do with its adjustment or survival under ordinary conditions. It is quite possible that in its ordinary way of life a worm never does learn anything and has no chance to learn until we lift it from the mud and give it the special advantages of a higher education. One may say that only modern science makes it possible for a worm to realize its full intellectual potential.

Although learning may not be important to a flatworm, the fact that it learns is interesting to us. Particularly interesting is the odd fact that the brain does not seem to be the place where the effects of the worm's learning are stored. McConnell, Jacobson, and Kimble "taught" worms by repeatedly exposing them to a bright light for two seconds before the onset of an electric shock. After a while, the worms twitched whenever the light came on, before the shock. This is somewhat the same as if you were to blink because someone pointed a water pistol at your face. It seems to be a clear case of what is called conditioned-response learning. When the habit was firmly set, some of the worms were cut in half. The head ends grew new tails, and the tail ends grew new heads, with that vermian regenerative vigor which we can only envy. Control worms were trained in the same manner, but they were not divided. When the worms were tested four weeks later, the old heads, the old tails, and the control worms all gave evidence of "remembering" the old habit, and the tails were just as good at remembering as were the heads or the intact controls.

The data of the experiment are shown in Table 9-1. Original training scores and retraining scores are given, for both experimental and control animals. Each score in this table is the total number of trials until the conditioned response occurs in 23 of 25 trials. For example, where you see a "24" as a retraining score, this means that the animal missed its cue only

TABLE 9-1. Training and retraining scores of flatworms in a conditioned-response experiment described in the text.

| | EXPERIMENTAL ANIMALS | | | | CONTROL ANIMALS | |
	Original Training	Retraining Heads	Tails		Original Training	Retraining
E-1	99	50	51	C-1	123	24
E-2	191	37	24	C-2	153	25
E-3	97	48	72	C-3	195	62
E-4	83	35	44	C-4	131	43
E-5	200	30	25	C-5	325	45
Means	134	40	43.2		185.4	39.8

Source: J. V. McConnell, A. L. Jacobson, and D. P. Kimble, "Effects of Regeneration upon Retention of a Conditioned Response in the Planarian," *Journal of Comparative and Physiological Psychology,* 52 (1959), 1–5.

once in 24 times after 4 weeks without rehearsal. One of the intact animals has such a score, but so has one of the tails which had to regenerate a new head. Evidently there has been considerable retention of the effects of training, and there is little to choose between the performance of the heads, the tails, and the intact animals.

This unexpected result is not altogether out of line with what happens in the lower mammals. For example, the psychologist K. S. Lashley showed that when a rat is taught to respond differently to circles and triangles, or to black squares and white squares, it does not seem possible to eliminate the habit by cutting away any one small portion of the brain; it seems as if the habit is stored in more than one place, or perhaps nowhere in particular. Many neurophysiologists now think that learning and memory depend on changes in molecular structure rather than on changed "connections" in the nervous system, and the humble flatworm may help us to solve this riddle. However, we wish only to analyze the data of Table 9-1 in a way which will show the relation between

The World of Probability

chance and the sum of squares. Because so few scores are involved, it should be easy to follow the analysis.

THE ANALYSIS OF SCATTER

First, without trying to prove anything, let us see how the sum of squares compares with the range or the sum of absolute deviations, which might also be used to measure scatter. Table 9-2 gives these three statistics for each group of scores in

TABLE 9-2. Some measures of score variation (range, sum of absolute deviations, and sum of squared deviations) for each column of scores in Table 9–1.

	RANGE	$\Sigma\,|X{-}\overline{X}|$	$\Sigma\,(X{-}\overline{X})^2$
EXPERIMENTAL ANIMALS			
Original training	117	246	12,800
Retraining, heads	20	36	298
Retraining, tails	48	74.8	1,590.8
CONTROL ANIMALS			
Original training	202	298.4	27,483.2
Retraining	38	61.2	998.8

Table 9-1. All three measures of scatter are consistent, in the sense that when one sample has a higher range than another, it also has a greater sum of absolute deviations and a greater sum of squares. This is not necessary, but it would usually be the case. However, although the extreme difference in ranges is about 10 to 1, and the extreme difference in sums of absolute deviations is about 8 to 1, there is a difference of about 90 to 1 between the corresponding sums of squares. The reason for this contrast is that the range and the sum of absolute deviations are measuring effects, but the sum of squares is measuring the strength of chance influences which produced

these effects. Chance influences, as we know, tend to balance out. Therefore they produce effects which are slight compared with what would be produced by a directed force of the same intensity.

Our reason for saying that the sums of squares shown in Table 9-2 reflect only chance influences is because each of them is based on a group of scores which are alike insofar as the experimental conditions are concerned. This means that if the experiment is properly designed and conducted, the scores within each group differ only in chance respects.

Evidently these chance influences are much stronger for some groups of scores than for others. The sums of squares are relatively large for the two series of original training scores and relatively small for the three series of retraining scores. This is quite reasonable. It means that the training has brought about more consistent performance, just as drilling a company of recruits will cause each man to modify his natural stride, so that they all come to march in the same tempo. The training which the worms received increased the importance of the light as a signal for behavior, and therefore it reduced the relative importance of all chance influences. (See the left-hand side of Figure 2.)

The total for the sums of squares of all five series of scores is 43,171. We will call this the *within-groups* sum of squares, because the method of calculation was to take each group by itself and consider only deviations from the group mean. The within-groups sum is sometimes called the "error sum," because only chance influences are responsible for the differences on which it is based.

Another way to calculate a sum of squares for the same twenty-five scores would be to disregard the groups altogether, find the overall mean, and take deviations from that. This method amounts to saying that the basis for classifying the scores into different groups is of no importance, and that all

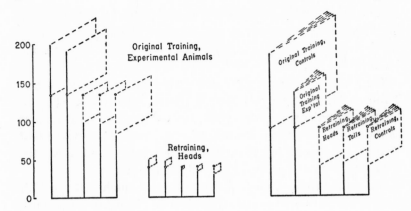

FIGURE 2. Schematic representation of the calculation of squares: (*left*), "within" squares for 2 groups of 5 scores each; (*right*), "between" squares for 5 groups of 5 scores each. In each figure, the row of small circles represents the mean value from which deviations are calculated.

differences among the scores are due to chance. We will call the result of this method the grand sum of squares. In the present case it turns out to be 134,350, which is considerably more than the within-sum. As a matter of fact, the grand sum must always be greater than the within-sum, for a reason which we may state in two different ways, which fundamentally mean the same thing.

(1) For any set of scores, the sum of squared deviations from their own mean, i.e., the within-sum, must be smaller than the sum of squared deviations from any other point. The proof of this formal mathematical statement is given in Appendix B.

(2) The grand sum is based not only on deviations which are due to chance influences, but also on those which are due to systematic differences among the groups, that is, differences in treatments or experimental variables. In other words, the grand sum has two components: an error component, the

within-sum, and a treatments component, which we call the between-groups sum of squares, or more briefly, the *between-sum*.

In this case, the between-sum is most readily obtained by subtracting the within-sum from the grand sum, which leaves 91,171. However, it may also be found directly, because the contribution which each score makes to it is equal to the squared difference between the group mean and the overall mean. (This follows from the second part of the proof in Appendix B, and it is illustrated schematically in the right-hand side of Figure 2.)

We get a somewhat clearer picture when we change the within-sum and the between-sum into proportions. In this example, the first represents 32 per cent and the second 68 per cent of the grand sum. The first is an error ratio, and the second a differentiation ratio. The differentiation ratio expresses the strength of the forces which are responsible for differences among the groups as a proportion of all the forces which are responsible for differences among the individual scores. It is true that chance is responsible for some of the group differentiation, but if the number of scores in each group is reasonably large, it is not too far from the mark to say that the size of the differentiation ratio does express the influence of the experimental treatments. (Certain adjustments, which we shall not discuss in detail, are desirable when the groups are small. They would not appreciably affect what we are discussing.) The symbol which is used to represent the differentiation ratio is η^2, eta square, and that is all the name it usually receives.

The fact that a differentiation ratio is larger than an error ratio, as in this case, has no great importance in itself. The important question is how large it is by comparison with what might be expected as a purely chance result, under similar circumstances—that is, with the same number of scores divided into the same number of groups and with "chance" operating at the level of intensity indicated by the within-sum. In this chapter, we shall make only some rough empirical estimates of what to expect.

First, let us compute a differentiation ratio for the three series of retraining scores—that is, leaving out the original training scores, which were so much more variable. This is the result:

Grand sum of squares	2,924	
Within-sum	2,888	(98.8 per cent)
Between-sum	36	(1.2 per cent)

In this case, training has been similar, but some scores are for divided animals, and others for controls. The very small value of the differentiation ratio indicates that this difference in treatment has had virtually no influence on retention of the effects of training. We may assume that the differentiation ratio in this case has a chance value—but the situation is one in which the scope of chance influences has been greatly reduced by the uniform prior treatment.

Another kind of comparison is even more valuable. It is perfectly feasible for us to estimate the chance level of between-scatter in this situation by a simple, common-sense method. If we want to know to what extent groups will be differentiated by chance, the most direct way is to throw all the scores into a hat and draw them out by chance. Let us do this for all twenty-five scores.

Instead of using a hat, we use the table of random digits. (Remember, you can do this with the telephone directory if you like.) We give each score a two-place code number, and then, starting somewhere in the middle of the table of random digits, we read off successive two-place numbers. The scores corresponding to the first five code numbers to appear will form the first group, those corresponding to the next five will form the second group, and so on. When this method is used, pure chance decides how the scores of individual animals are assembled by groups. Of the millions of possible reassortments, this is the one which I obtained.

Group I:	37,	24,	25,	123,	97
Group II:	99,	44,	200,	50,	45
Group III:	195,	51,	24,	25,	325
Group IV:	43,	30,	83,	191,	62
Group V:	48,	35,	72,	153,	131

When we calculate sums of squares for these groups this is the result:

Grand sum of squares	134,350	
Within-sum	124,113	(92 per cent)
Between-sum	10,237	(8 per cent)

These two empirical tests show how unlikely it is that more than a small part of the between-sum in the actual experiment was due to chance.

Let us review the path we followed in this chapter, up to this point. (1) We recognize that the scattering of scores is important and that we need to do something about it. (2) We propose to use the sum of squared deviations as a measure of scatter. (3) We recognize that within-scatter is not influenced by the experimental treatments and can only be measuring chance influences. (4) Therefore the difference between within-scatter and total-scatter measures all effects of the experimental treatments. (5) We see in practice that this remainder, the between-scatter, is relatively low when the assortment of scores is by chance and relatively high when a strong experimental variable differentiates the groups. (6) We call the ratio of between-scatter to total-scatter the differentiation ratio. It is that proportion of the grand sum of squares which results from the operation of factors (including experimental treatments) which differ from group to group. It will be larger when the effect of the experimental treatments is strong and smaller when that effect is weak, relative to the strength of chance influences.

UP IN SMOKE

In the experiment which we used to illustrate this discussion, the results were so clear that they scarcely needed statistical analysis. The differentiation ratio is usually used to study less obvious relationships and with more extensive data. Therefore we shall give another and more typical example, in brief. The scores in Table 9-3 are grade-point averages for 187 male students at Texas Christian University. The students have been classified according to their smoking habits, and, for convenience, the scores within each category have been grouped into score classes. A code value (x') is used to represent the score for each class. (Since we are only interested in a ratio, the absolute value of the scores is not important.) Using the coded scores, the analysis leads to the following sums of squares:

Grand sum of squares	1081.7	
Within-sum	997.2	(92.2 per cent)
Between-sum	84.5	(7.8 per cent)

We express this result in words by saying that about 8 per cent of the sum of squares is associated with smoking habits. Perhaps you would be inclined to dismiss this as a chance result, but that would be a mistake. It can be shown that, because of the large number of scores in this investigation, the result is one which would not occur by chance even 1 time in 100. (Later we shall show this by another method, on Page

TABLE 9-3. Grade-point averages of 187 male students at Texas Christian University, in categories based on smoking habits.

GRADE-POINT AVERAGE	x'	NONSMOKERS	LESS THAN 1 PACK A DAY	1 PACK A DAY	MORE THAN 1 PACK A DAY
4.00	+7	1			
3.75–3.99	+6	3			
3.50–3.74	+5	3		1	
3.25–3.49	+4	5		1	
3.00–3.24	+3	6	5		
2.75–2.99	+2	8	2	5	1
2.50–2.74	+1	18	2	3	4
2.25–2.49	0	12	4	9	6
2.00–2.24	−1	16	4	10	5
1.75–1.99	−2	6	7	12	2
1.50–1.74	−3	6		8	1
1.25–1.49	−4		3	1	2
1.00–1.25	−5	2		1	
0.75–0.99	−6	1			
0.50–0.74	−7		1		
TOTALS		87	28	51	21

Source: Data provided, in personal communication, by the investigators, S. B. Sells and Nurhan Findikyan.

98   *The World of Probability*

145.) These data show that there is a real relationship between smoking habits and academic performance.

This does not mean that smoking, as such, influences grades. We speak only of a functional relationship and not of cause. Inspection of Table 9-3 will show that most of the effect can be traced to the fact that students with exceptionally high grade-point averages tend to be nonsmokers. One possible explanation for this is that they are more highly motivated learners, who take knowledge seriously, including recent scientific information about effects of smoking. Another might be that it is very difficult for anyone who resides in a fraternity house either to maintain a high grade-point average or to remain a nonsmoker. To choose between these and other possible explanations, further research would be needed.

Although the differentiation ratio shows that there is a statistical dependence between smoking habits and grades, it also shows that this dependence is weak. More important determinants of grades are academic aptitude, industry, health, and opportunity for study. When a relationship is "very significant" in a statistical sense, this does not necessarily mean that it is also very important. The differentiation ratio in this case may equally be read to mean that "at least 92 per cent of all the influences which determine academic grades of male college students are not associated with smoking habits."

With just a little more work, the differentiation ratio can be calculated in terms of mean squares, instead of sums of squares. That has no value in itself, but the changed plan of work would provide an opportunity—which we shall not explain in detail—to make a suitable allowance for the tendency of the differentiation ratio to somewhat overstate the strength of the experimental variable. In this example, the "differentiation ratio without bias" would be .063 instead of .078. The difference between the two values would be greater if there were fewer observations available and less if there were more. The adjustment, therefore, is not very important in most cases where the use of a differentiation ratio is appropriate, and the method of adjustment is one which would only emphasize further the main point of this chapter—that it is possible to assign a portion of the sum of squares to each influence which tends to differentiate the scores.

Chapter 10

WHEN SCORES
ARE INDISCRETE

•

ONCE AGAIN, we pick up the study of probability distributions, this time to learn about the normal distribution. Like the Poisson distribution, the normal distribution is only a special case of the binomial distribution, but it plays a much more important part in statistical work.

A binomial distribution with any fixed value of N will contain $N + 1$ different or discrete scores, each of which recurs with a certain frequency. Values intermediate between these scores are not possible. We may talk about 2.5 heads as the expected value in tossing five coins, but the actual number of heads in any sample must be an integer. This has been true for each theoretical distribution discussed so far. Whether we have been talking about coins, people, or neurons, the score has always been arrived at by counting events.

Any of these distributions can be graphically represented by a bar diagram, in which the height of each bar represents the relative frequency of one of the possible scores. Figure 3 (*a*) represents the binomial distribution for $N = 4$, $p = .5$. It consists of only 5 bars, because there are only 5 possible scores in

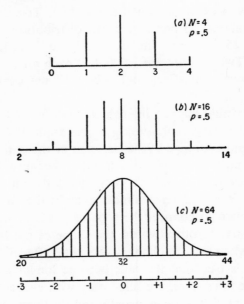

FIGURE 3. The normal distribution as a limit of the binomial. The bars show discrete distributions for $N = 4$, $N = 16$, and $N = 64$, with $p = .5$ in each case. The curve in the lowest figure shows the continuous distribution approached as N grows without limit. The standard scale at the bottom is explained on Page 108.

the distribution. The probability of any nonintegral score is zero. Therefore such a distribution is also called *discontinuous*.

As the value of N increases, the relative frequencies of very high and very low scores become so small that for practical purposes they can be disregarded. Figure 3 (*b*) represents the distribution for $N = 16$ and $p = .5$. Only thirteen bars are shown, but these represent 99.95 per cent of the distribution. The four bars which have been left out could scarcely be shown even as bumps on the base line. Together, they make up only about .05 per cent of the distribution.

Only 25 bars are shown in Figure 3 (c), for $N = 64$, $p = .5$. Twenty bars are left out at each end, 40 all together, but the omission affects only about .2 per cent of the entire distribution.

What would happen in such a graph for $N = 999$? Ninety-six vertical bars, representing scores from 452 to 547, inclusive, would comprise 99.76 per cent of the entire distribution. We do not show this distribution, because it would add nothing new. If a smooth curve were drawn to connect the 96 bars, it would have almost exactly the same shape as a curve drawn to connect the tops of the 25 bars in the graph for $N = 64$. In other words, the shape of the binomial distribution, when $p = .5$, changes very little after N becomes fairly large. It is true that the tails become longer and longer, but they, like fairy tales, are filled only with events so improbable that in practice we can usually ignore them. In a graph for $N = 10,000$, the tops of 301 bars would mark out the same distinctive curve, and again only about ¼ per cent of the total distribution would lie in the 9,700 bars comprising the tails.

This is a time to throw discreteness to the winds! Why be concerned with particular values of N, and the relative height of each individual bar, if the end result is only imperceptibly different? As N grows without limit, the number of scores even under a small segment of this curve also becomes unlimited. The scores, which were once discretely arranged in neat piles, are now crowded like points on a line, and we say that they form a *continuous* series, one next to the other with no gap between. The probabilities which are exact for this limiting case are good approximations for every case in which N is large, when $p = .5$.

As a matter of fact, we arrive at the same result even when p does not equal .5, provided that N is great beyond all measure. You have already observed (for example, in tables 4-3 and 4-4) that when p and q are not equal, the probability distribution is not symmetrical. However, with large N this skew is mostly in the tails, and it shows hardly at all in the central portion of the distribution. When N is very large, the distribution is symmetrical for practical purposes, even though p and q are quite unequal. As N approaches infinity, the distribution approaches normal form for any fixed value of p, no no matter how small. (In the case of the Poisson distribution, you will remember, p was not fixed, but became smaller and smaller, without limit, as N became larger and larger. That is why it retained its skew. Yet even the Poisson distribution tends toward normal form when Np, or $\overline{X}$, becomes very large.)

This means that the normal distribution is a close approximation to the shape of any binomial distribution with large N and moderate p. It is also the characteristic form for any set of scores which result from the action of many independent and equally important causal factors. A fine example of this is a lengthy quiz made up of true–false questions, given to a large class of students, and on a subject about which they know almost nothing. Under these conditions, the scores will have a near-normal distribution (see Figure 4 (a)). If the questions are in multiple-choice form, so that the probability of a correct guess is, say, .2 instead of .5, the distribution of chance results will be strongly skewed for a short quiz (see Figure 4 (b)), but it will again approach normal form if there are a great many questions (Figure 4 (c)). Somewhat ironically, teachers frequently assume that the scores and grades should still be normally distributed even after the students have been instructed, but there is no warrant in statistics for this opinion. There is nothing in the nature of the educational process which determines that its results must be distributed in a random manner.

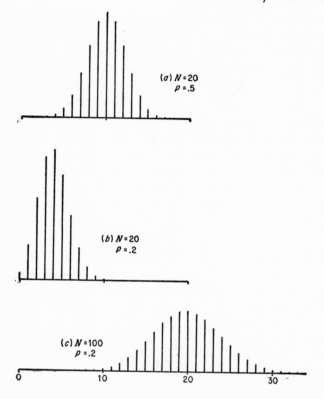

FIGURE 4. Distributions of chance scores on 3 tests: (*a*) 20 true–false items, (*b*) 20 multiple-choice items, (*c*) 100 multiple-choice items.

NORMAL PROBABILITY

The normal curve is most simply described as "bell shaped." However, this phrase does not help us to understand its nature. To study it, we may begin by comparing it with the function $(1/e)^{\overline{X}}$. In that function, the proportional decline in any segment is exactly the same as for any other segment which covers the same distance on the base line. This is the phenomenon which we have previously described as "constant rate of shrinkage."

The normal curve seems at first glance to defy attempts at a simple description of this sort, because it seems to change its character in mid-course. It looks very much like a double ski run. We may take off in either direction from the rounded central knoll, down a slope which steepens by imperceptible degrees, until it is pitching steeply downward; but then at a given point this trend is reversed, the downward acceleration progressively declines, and as we near the base of the "mountain" we are carried into an endless gentle glide. What secret unites the rounded top, steep sides, and gentle lower slopes into a single function?

Actually, the nature of the change which is taking place is always the same. The eye is deceived, for it sees "magnitudes" where it should look for "proportions." The very simple fact is that the curve of normal probability declines by ever-increasing proportions, in obedience to this rule: at any distance from the mean, the proportional drop in a very short segment of the curve is exactly n times as great as it was in a similar segment, at $1/n$th the distance from the mean. If one of the segments is twice as far from the mean as the other, then the proportional decline is twice as great; if three times as far, then three times as great; and so on.

This statement surprises us, because those long tails of the normal distribution, which stretch out to infinity, seem so deceptively flat. The fact is that relative heights within the tails, for a given difference in score, differ much more than near the middle of the distribution. In this respect, the normal curve only carries out "to the nth degree," and with complete regularity from crown to toe, something which is already present in the Pascal triangle. There, too, as one moves outward from the center of any of its distributions, each step is greater than the one before proportionwise, although it is often smaller as a matter of numerical difference.

What we witness here, in place of "steady shrinkage," is an

"accelerated depletion." After all, shrinkage is not the only problem our shirts contend with, when we send them to the laundry. In successive washings, a shirt may shrink always by the same proportion, yet it may lose its fabric in ever-increasing proportions. If the loss of fabric is half as great, proportionwise, on the nth wash as on the $(2n)$th wash, one-third as great as on the $(3n)$th wash, and so forth, that is "normal." As this process continues, the actual quantity of lint removed will at the beginning be greater and greater on each wash, but there will come a time when the shirt is so thin that each succeeding wash will remove less lint than the one preceding, rather than more. That is the point at which the normal curve ceases to become steeper, moving outward from the center, and gradually begins to flatten its course.

In order to express this pattern as a mathematical function, we must first select an appropriate unit by which to measure distances from the mean. The ordinary scores which served us in the binomial and Poisson distributions have lost their usefulness and must be replaced by some system of relative scores. The same point under this curve which may be "20" in one normal distribution may be "6.34" in another and "1065" in a third. If the heights of men are normally distributed, so also may be the lengths of herring and the weights of elephants. We need to invent a unit of measurement which will apply equally well to any normal distribution, and which will always give each score its proper place under the curve.

For this purpose, we select as standard a unit which arises quite naturally out of the curve's distinctive shape. The distance from the mean to that point, on either side, where the curve attains its steepest slope, is called a *standard deviation*. This is the "point of inflection" where big bites give way to smaller bites and increasing proportion just ceases to be increasing quantity. The symbol for a standard deviation is the small Greek letter sigma, σ.

As a rough approximation, this distance is one-fifth of the

range in a random sample of 100 scores from a normal distribution; in a sample of 500 scores, the range will be about 6 times the standard deviation. For the full distribution, the standard deviation is exactly equal to the "root mean square," that is, the square root of the mean squared deviation. Expressed as a formula,

$$\sigma = \sqrt{\frac{\Sigma x^2}{n}}.$$

In other words, this is a score which has a valid claim to being a sort of representative score in any distribution—as that score which, being squared, becomes the mean square of the distribution. This formula is used to extend the concept of the standard deviation to all distributions, of any form whatever. It is the definition of a standard deviation.

Every other score can be expressed as a fraction or a multiple of this standard unit, just as any physical length, whether it be measured in inches, miles, or astronomical units (that is, in terms of the average distance of the earth from the sun), can also be expressed as a fraction or a multiple of the standard unit of length which we call a meter. A score which has been restated in this way is called a standard score. The symbol for a standard score is z.

Now we can give a mathematical formula for the normal curve. If z stands for a given score expressed in standard form, and if y stands for relative frequency, then the relative frequency of any score in a normal distribution, as a proportion of the frequency of the mean score, is given by this formula:

$$y\{z\} = (1/e)^{z^2/2}.$$

This formula can be solved with the help of Table 8-4, if we first find the value of $z^2/2$ and use it in place of $\overline{X}$ to enter the table. For example, to find the relative frequency of a score of $\pm 0.8\sigma$, we first calculate: $(0.8)^2/2 = .32$. In the table we find that $(1/e)^{.3} = .741$, and $(1/e)^{.02} = .980$, whence $(1/e)^{.32}$ equals their product, $.726$. This means that scores in a very narrow range about 0.8σ from the mean, in either direction, will occur about 73 per cent as often as scores in an equally narrow range around the mean.

It is an interesting fact that in any binomial distribution, the standard deviation also equals $\sqrt{Npq}$. (The proof of this statement appears in Appendix D, but it rests on a rule proved in Appendix C, which will be discussed in Chapter 10. So for the time being you will have to take it on faith, or test it empirically.) By this formula, the standard deviations of the binomial distributions in Figure 4 are, respectively, 1, 2, and 4. Now you can see that the distributions were so drawn that they all have standard deviations represented by equal lengths on the horizontal scale. The standard scale at the bottom of the figure applies equally to all of them. On that scale, the score of 12 in the distribution for $N = 16$ has a value which is stated as $+ 2\sigma$, while the score of 24 in the distribution for $N = 64$ has a value of -2σ.

In this way, the use of standard scores removes the ambiguity which comes from using different scales for different distributions. When we want to compare scores in different distributions, it is always best to use standard scores. One hundred pounds is a big fish, but a small elephant; as a standard score, it will be a large positive deviation in one distribution and a negative deviation in the other.

APPLYING NORMAL PROBABILITIES

In workaday applications, we do not need to know the relative frequency of a particular score in a normal distribution as often as we need to know the cumulative frequency (that is, the joint probability) of all scores above or below a certain standard score, or between certain standard scores. Often, when we consider a certain experimental outcome (for example, the chick in Chapter 2 pecking at a triangle 8 times out of 10), we want to know what the probability is for obtaining either this outcome or any more extreme outcome (that is, either 8 or 9 or 10 pecks at circle *or* triangle). To answer such a question, what we must know is not the height of the normal curve at a given point, but the proportional area under the curve beyond that point.

The way to construct such a table is to calculate relative frequencies for narrow strips of the probability surface, and then "integrate" or sum them. Since the normal distribution is continuous, calculus is used to do this for infinitely many slices, each of infinitesimal width. But one can get very much the same answers without calculus, by pretending the curve is discontinuous, and calculating relative frequencies for standard scores at intervals of one-tenth of a standard deviation, taking their sum as the total of all frequencies and changing them into proportions of that total. This is equivalent to using a discrete distribution, with $N = 400$, in place of the continuous normal distribution. The resulting table will be accurate to three places in all its entries. (After all, if a discrete distribution with large N could not be used to approximate the normal distribution, of what good would the normal distribution be to approximate discrete distributions?)

Table 10-1 is called a table of areas of the normal probability surface. It is one of the tables most frequently used in statistical work, and therefore we put it in a handy place for reference, on the inside back cover. In that table we find answers to questions like these:

(1) In a normal distribution, what proportion of all the scores deviate from the expected value by more than $\pm 1\sigma$? (Slightly less than one-third, that is, twice .159.)

(2) What proportion deviate by more than $\pm 2\sigma$? (4.6 per cent, that is, twice .023.)

TABLE 10-1. Normal Probability. (*a*) The proportion of the normal probability surface in the smaller portion which is cut off by $\pm x/\sigma$. (*b*) The proportion of the normal probability surface in both tails, beyond certain critical values of $|x/\sigma|$ which are commonly used in statistical tests.

(*a*)

$\pm x/\sigma$	p	$\pm x/\sigma$	p	$\pm x/\sigma$	p
0.0	.500	1.0	.159	2.0	.023
0.1	.460	1.1	.136	2.1	.018
0.2	.421	1.2	.115	2.2	.014
0.3	.382	1.3	.097	2.3	.011
0.4	.345	1.4	.074	2.4	.008
0.5	.309	1.5	.067	2.5	.006
0.6	.274	1.6	.055	2.6	.005
0.7	.242	1.7	.045	2.7	.003
0.8	.212	1.8	.036	2.8	.003
0.9	.184	1.9	.029	2.9	.002

(*b*)

$|x/\sigma|$	p
1.96	.05
2.58	.01
3.29	.001

(3) What proportion have deviations greater than $+1\sigma$ and less than $+2\sigma$? (13.6 per cent, an answer obtained by subtracting .023 from .159.)

(4) What proportion lies between -1σ and -0.5σ? (15 per cent.)

In a supplementary table beneath the main table, we give the proportion of the total surface which lies outside certain critical deviation values in *both* tails of the distribution. When we use this portion of the table, we have in mind some degree of "reasonable doubt" which we are willing to tolerate—

desiring to be of sound judgment, but mindful of the frailty of human experiment. If the chosen level of reasonable doubt is 1 chance in 20 of being wrong, then the critical scores are at ±1.96 standard deviations, because these are the values which enclose the middle 95 per cent of the probability surface. If we are unwilling to tolerate more than a 1 per cent doubt, the cutoff points are at ±2.58 standard deviations, because these points enclose 99 per cent of the surface, cutting off .5 per cent in each tail. The use of these critical points will appear repeatedly in all of our discussions from now on.

A few pages back, we said that the normal distribution is the characteristic form for any set of scores which result from the action of many independent and equally important factors. Whenever there is a wide range of scores, we know that many causal factors have been at work, and if the scores tend to be normally distributed, with a single mode, the indications are that no one causal factor is predominant.

The number of natural phenomena which are distributed in a normal or nearly normal manner is not nearly so great as one might at first imagine. Most of the examples one reads about, like the size of peas, the height of men, the width of the skull or length of the forearm, are measurements of the size attained by growing things. Others, like human intelligence, are simply scores which result from assembling results of many separate test items, a process which will tend to produce a normal distribution even when the sampling is not done in a normal universe. Most psychologists today agree that what we call intelligence is a medley of many special aptitudes and skills, which tend in general to be positively related to one another—that is, an individual who does well in any one of them is more likely than not to do well in almost any other you can name. But we have so little evidence as yet concerning the distributions of the various special aptitudes and such poor success as yet in constructing intelligence tests for either the very dull or the very bright that we can hardly make any assertion about the distribution of intelligence other than that it is *assumed* to be normal by most persons working in that field and that this assumption is useful for their purposes. The fact that intelligence test scores tend to be normally distributed is evidence of the skill of those who construct the tests and not of any fundamental biological reality.

However, the importance of the normal distribution does not in the least depend on whether natural phenomena are or are not normally distributed. What is important is that the results of experiments—like the results of lengthy tests—tend to be distributed in that manner. For example, incomes are not normally distributed, but suppose that every day for a year you stop 20 people on the street and ask each one to report on his income. You would get different results each day, but the distribution of average incomes, day by day, would be very close to normal. Opinions, also, are not normally distributed, but if each day you ask twenty persons selected at random whether they favor giving the vote to eighteen-year-olds, the proportion of those saying "yes" will be different from one day to the next, but the distribution of day-by-day proportions will be approximately normal. This is because it is a matter of chance whether the next man you stop on the street is John Doe or Jack Spratt, and many such chance results influence each day's result. The same thing is true in any scientific investigation. If we repeat it many times, the results will never quite agree, but they will tend to be normally distributed. For this reason, the normal distribution is called "the law of error," and we can use it to judge how great an allowance for error we must make before arriving at conclusions based on experiments. This most important application of statistical method is the one which will concern us in Chapters 11 and 12.

Chapter 11

THE EXTENT OF
REASONABLE DOUBT

•

THERE IS AN OLD STORY about three blind men who traveled to India and were introduced to many of its wonders by a friendly *nabob*. They had heard about elephants and wanted to know what these great beasts were like, and so their host arranged an opportunity for them to satisfy their curiosity. When the first blind man reached out to touch the elephant, he took hold of an ear, and he reported to his friends: "The elephant is like a huge fan." The second took hold of the trunk and he immediately objected, "No, no! It is like a great snake." The third blind man reached out both hands and grasped one of the massive legs. "You are both wrong," he said, and added with great positiveness, "This elephant is like a tree."

Each had his own little sample of an elephant, and it is not surprising that they formed different opinions. We are amused, however, that they should express their views with such misplaced confidence. To protect ourselves from the same kind of mistake, we must know what happens when a certain amount of experience, which we call "a sample of n observations," is all the basis we have for forming a judgment about the population from which the sample was taken. If, like the blind men, we can form no opinion except to imagine that the population is just like the little sample which we know, how much confidence does that opinion deserve? Is it possible to define a criterion of reasonable doubt by which to guide our judgment?

You will recall that whenever we take even a small sample out of a large population, there is an enormous number of ways in which it may be selected. The observed sample is not merely a collection of random observations; viewed as a unit, it is also one random choice taken out of the universe of equally possible samples. Awareness of this fact should stop us from making foolish pronouncements based on limited experience. On the other hand, there is no need to strike a posture of total ignorance. Although we know nothing positively, we know a great deal as a matter of probability.

We can learn certain important rules about the universe of samples if we systematically study the results of sampling in a very small population, where it will be easy to keep track of all the results. For this purpose, imagine a top which has 5 flat sides and the opposite edges numbered 1 to 5, so that when we spin the top, there is an equal opportunity for any of these "scores" to appear. Since each of the possible scores is expected to occur as often as any other, we say that the probability distribution is rectangular. This is the parent population from which we shall select samples. For each sample size, we shall construct a universe which consists of the distribution of sums-of-scores in all possible samples of that size.

To do this, imagine a game in which each turn consists of spinning this top several times. We begin by considering the distribution of scores for two spins. The lowest possible score is 2, and the highest is 10. If you prepare a table of all the possible results, you will see that the frequencies of the various scores in this universe are as follows:

X	2	3	4	5	6	7	8	9	10
f_x	1	2	3	4	5	4	3	2	1

This probability distribution is shown in Figure 5 (a). It is called a triangular distribution because the frequencies fall off regularly, in direct proportion to distance from the mean. (However, it may be worth noting that even here the proportional decline in each successive step is greater than in the one before, moving outward from the mean.) This is the universe of sample sums, for $n = 2$.

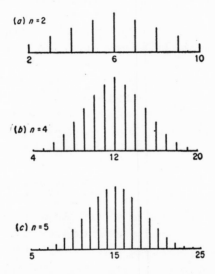

FIGURE 5. Distributions of sample sums for samples of different size drawn from a rectangular universe of 5 scores, 1 to 5.

If each turn of the game consists of three spins, the range of scores is from 3 to 15. Relative frequencies of these scores in the universe are as follows:

X	3	4	5	6	7	8	9	10	11	12	13	14	15
f_x	1	3	6	10	15	18	19	18	15	10	6	3	1

This is the universe of sample sums for $n = 3$. The simple regularity of the preceding example has been lost, but of course it is still true that each frequency, moving outward from the center, involves an increasing proportional decline from the one before.

The relative frequencies for scores in the universes which result from four spins and from five spins are shown in the Figure 5, (*b*) and (*c*). In the distribution for $n = 5$, the outline of the normal distribution is clearly suggested. The two extreme cases in that distribution, each occurring once in 3,125 times, are the buds from which will grow the long tails which are such a characteristic feature of the normal distribution and which shelter only those highly improbable events which we do not expect to meet in real experience.

It is clear that the universe of sums rapidly approaches normal form as the *n* of the sample increases. This is what we expect of any score which results from the accumulation of many chance events. On closer study, we also see that many characteristics of the universe of sums change in a very regular manner from one sample size to the next. The range of each sample universe is equal to *n* times the original range, which was 4. The mean of each sample universe is equal to *n* times the mean of the parent population, which was 3. These facts are almost obvious, and it can easily be demonstrated that they must apply to all sample universes, drawn from any populations whatever. However, we want to pay particular attention to the scatter of scores in these distributions. It will no longer be convenient to measure scatter by the sum of squares, as we did in Chapter 9, because the size of each universe is different, and therefore comparisons become difficult. Instead, we now take as our measure of scatter the *mean square,* which is also called *variance.* You will recall (from Page 107) that the mean square entered into the definition of the standard deviation. Variance is the standard deviation squared, and hence the symbol for variance is σ^2.

Do you also remember (from Appendix B) that the sum of squares is equal to the sum of squared scores less the squared sum of scores divided by their number? That is, $\Sigma x^2 = \Sigma X^2 - (\Sigma X)^2/n$. To find the mean square, each term in this formula must be divided by n, which gives this convenient computational formula:

$$\sigma^2 = \frac{\Sigma x^2}{n} = \frac{\Sigma X^2}{n} - \left(\frac{\Sigma X}{n}\right)^2 .$$

This formula can be expressed as follows: variance is the mean squared score less the squared mean score.

You can easily verify that the mean squared deviations of the sample universes which we have constructed are 2 (for the parent population), then 4, 6, 8, etc. From one sample to the next, the variance grows by an amount which is equal to the variance of the parent population from which the samples have been taken. Thus, the same simple rule which applies to the mean and the range also applies to the variance. The variance of a universe of sums, based on samples of size n, equals n times the variance of the parent population.

This remarkably simple rule will still hold true when the sample is made up of members which are taken from different parent distributions. If the rules of the game are to spin a 5-sided top, throw a 6-sided die, and then spin a 32-place roulette wheel, then the range of sums will be $4 + 5 + 31 = 40$; the mean of the universe of sums will be $3 + 3.5 + 16.5 = 23$; and the variance will be the sum of the variances for spinning a 5-sided top, throwing a 6-sided die, and spinning a 32-place roulette wheel. The proof of this important rule, which we shall call the *variance law,* is given in Appendix C.

Since variance is additive, it is also subtractive. That is, the total variance can be analyzed into parts, and portions of it can be traced to different sources. We did something like this in Chapter 9, where we analyzed a sum of squares into a within-sum, associated solely with error, and a between-sum, which is a maximum estimate of the strength of the experimental treatments. But that was only a beginning. Variance in performance on intelligence tests can be analyzed into a proportion which is attributable to differences in heredity and a proportion attributable to environmental influences. Variance in wheat production can be analyzed into a proportion which is due to differences in weather and a proportion due to the use of fertilizers. Variance in the number of runs yielded by baseball teams might be analyzed into a proportion which is due to differences in pitching skill, a proportion due to differences in strength of the infield, and a proportion which is due to differences in strength of the outfield. Variances in attendance at municipal art museums might be analyzed into a proportion due to quality of the exhibits, a proportion due to work of the publicity department, and a proportion which is seasonal. In every case, it would also be necessary to assign a proportion due to chance, that is, to factors which are not being studied. The analysis can also show "interaction," that is, it can show if the fertilizer is more effective in moist weather than in dry, if the infield is relatively more important to a good pitcher or a mediocre one, if the work of the publicity department is relatively more important in vacation seasons than at other times of the year. These are possibilities that we shall examine in our final chapter, on new strategies for science.

At present, our goal is to learn what we can infer about a population from the evidence of one sample. With this purpose in mind, we are learning first about the universe of samples. The variance law applies to the sums in that universe, but there is, of course, a definite relationship between sums and means in the same sample. A mean is simply a sum, divided by n, the number in the sample.

If the sums are normally distributed, so are the means, but of course they will have a smaller range and a smaller variance. Since each sum is n times as great as the mean of the same sample, the range of sums is n times as great as the range of means. However, the relation between the variance of sums and the variance of means is not quite so direct.

To appreciate the difference, just suppose that the heights of the 10,000 French recruits arrayed in columns in Table 7-1 had been stated in *pieds* (feet) instead of in *pouces* (inches). To make this change, each man's score would be divided by 12. Since each square foot contains 144 square inches, the sum of squares will be reduced by a factor of 144, not by a factor of 12. Changing from a universe of sums to a universe of means is a similar operation, because each mean is a sum divided by n. Therefore, to convert a variance of sums into a variance of means, we must divide by n^2. That makes it equal to the population variance divided by n. This is the formula which we have been seeking:

$$\sigma^2\bar{\mathrm{x}} = \sigma^2{}_{pop}/n.$$

The means of small samples, gathered under the same conditions, will scatter widely; the means of large samples will agree more closely. If we take the square root of each side, the formula gives the value of the standard deviation of the universe of means, which is called the *standard error of the mean*:

$$\sigma_{\bar{\mathrm{x}}} = \sigma_{pop}/\sqrt{n}.$$

These formulas reflect both the skill and the industry of the investigator, for they show that the allowance he must make for experimental error grows bigger in direct proportion to the inconsistency of his observations, and it grows smaller as he increases their number.

These equations give theoretical values which are exactly right for the universe. Usually we are forced to estimate them, using the sample variance in place of the unknown population variance. Under these conditions, the formulas still give very good estimates if the sample is large. The special problem which arises with small samples is discussed in Appendix E. Our discussion will continue as if we were concerned only with large samples.

The result we have reached is one which has the greatest practical importance. In a serious scientific report, it is rare to find a mean value which is not accompanied by its standard error. Let us see why.

CONFIDENCE LIMITS

A score is like a house address. Fifth Avenue can be drab or glamorous, depending on the town. If we know nothing about the distribution from which a score comes, the score itself has no meaning. Conversely, when we know the characteristics of the distribution, it is like having a map of the town, which enables us to locate any address. What is true of a score is also true of the expected value of a sample. It is one member of a universe. It has meaning only in terms of the universe to which it belongs.

This is what we know about the universe of sample means: (1) it has the same mean as the parent population; (2) it has a shape which is near-normal; and (3) it has a variance which is equal to the population variance divided by n. In other words, it is a normally distributed collection of error, or false returns. Our knowledge is enough so that we can say how great a proportion of all the returns miss their mark by more than some stipulated amount. We can say, for example, that there are 95 chances in 100 that the bird-in-hand, the one sample on which we must base our opinion, did not miss by more than 1.96 standard errors, and there are 99 chances in 100 that it did not miss by more than 2.58 standard errors.

Usually, whether for convenience or as a matter of custom, we make our statements the other way around: there are only 5 chances in 100 that the population mean differs from the sample mean by more than 1.96 standard errors; there is only 1 chance in 100 that it differs by more than 2.58 standard errors. These are statements of a measured confidence. We never say that the population mean has a certain value, but only that it lies within a certain interval, at a certain level of probability, which, for the purpose at hand, we regard as a reasonable doubt. What falls inside these limits we accept as reasonable; whatever lies beyond them we exclude as improbable.

The proper report of a scientific finding is always in a form which permits the reader to judge the range of values within which the true value probably falls. When a physicist reports that the mass of a neutral pi-meson equals 264.2 ± 0.5 times the mass of an electron, he means that 264.2 is the mean value in the sample of his observations, but the number and the variance of those observations were such that the standard error of measurement equals 0.5. Therefore there are 68 chances in 100 that the true value lies between 263.7 and 264.7, and about 1 chance in 20 that it lies outside the range of values from 263.2 to 265.2. When a geologist reports that the great basalt columns at Devil's Postpile, near Yosemite National Park, have an age of 0.94 ± 0.16 million years, he says in effect that it is improbable that these giant crystals have existed for more than 1.25 million years, or for less than 0.63 million years. When an archaeologist reports that carbon-14 dating fixes the age of bones taken from the floor of an ancient camp site at 1420 B.C. ± 125 years, we recognize that this suggests a range of about 490 years for the actual date of the hunting party of which the bones are evidence and that it is improbable that the true date is earlier than 1175 B.C. or later than 1665 B.C.

We fully expect that statements like these, which are made at the 95 per cent level of confidence, will be wrong about once in 20 times. Using the 99 per cent level, we will be wrong about once in 100 times. To be "sure," we can extend the confidence interval to 99.9 per cent limits (3.29 standard errors), but this is only trading one kind of uncertainty for another; it is always an easy matter to be right by being vague and indefinite. Usually it is better to take a higher risk of error, just so we know what risk we take and wait for further evidence. When the archaeologist, for example, has an opportunity to compare the results of this find with those of another which appears to be of the same culture, he will seek the most consistent explanation for both. He will remember, then, that although it is "probable" that this prehistoric hunting party took place between 1665 and 1175 B.C., there is a long chance (1 in 100) that it took place any time between 1100 and 1750 B.C., and it is barely possible (1 chance in 1000) that it took place any time between 1010 and 1830 B.C. Of course, if the additional evidence from the second find compels him to accept a date outside the relatively narrow 5 per cent interval, it will also indicate whether the upper or lower portion of the wider interval is to be preferred, so it will lead, as all new evidence should, to a reduced range of error.

When the confidence interval is broader than we like, there are two ways to reduce it. The first is wider experience. By taking four times as many observations, one can expect to cut the range of probable values for the mean by half. The other way is to achieve better control over error variables, and thus attain more consistent measurements. As stated earlier: the formula for the standard error of the mean reflects the skill of the investigator in the numerator and his industry in the denominator. Our confidence cannot rest on one without the other.

Chapter 12

ASK THE
IMPROBABLE!

●

No REASONABLE MAN expects to discover complete truth. The path of science is an ever-ascending trail, and each time that we get to the top of one rise, we are sure to discover another rocky ascent ahead. Truth is "the other side of the mountain," beyond our farthest reach. What science discovers is never more than probability.

Error can be identified with certainty. The probability that the moon is made of green cheese approaches zero, and the probability that it was colonized by Leif Ericson is no greater. It seems highly probable, on the other hand, that the Vikings did visit North America, and it is not beyond possibility that accumulated evidence may someday place Leif himself on the present site of the Boston common in the year A.D. 1000, with high probability. But neither this nor any other event of more than trivial consequence can ever be established with complete certainty by the mere evidence of our senses and consensus of interpretations. What happens, as evidence accumulates, is that any alternative explanation becomes more and more improbable until at last we reject them all completely and declare that one hypothesis alone is acceptable.

That is the method of science. Not to strive for certainty, but to demonstrate improbability. Each great theory becomes a springboard for advance when men discover its inadequacies and state new hypotheses for further questioning. Science phrases each hypothesis only to question it, to cast reasonable doubt on it, and then to replace it with something which is for the time being less demonstrably improbable. Whatever the goal of science may be, its method is not to seek truth, but to ask the improbable.

In statistics, this general method takes a special form and special name: the "null hypothesis." The null hypothesis is a kind of reasoning by the method called *reductio ad absurdum,* that is, it disproves a proposition by showing how absurd, how improbable it is. Whenever we want to demonstrate the reality of an observed difference, or the reality of an experimental effect, we pretend ("for the sake of argument") that the whole thing is just a matter of chance, and then we go about proving that the events we have witnessed are improbable under that assumption. If it is sufficiently implausible that what happened was a chance event, in a universe regulated by chance, then we abandon the hypothesis that the effect we have been investigating is "null." We reject the null hypothesis because it is improbable, not because we can "prove" any alternative. It is the task of this chapter to show how the principles developed in Chapter 11 can be extended to test a null hypothesis shaped by the evidence of two samples.

Many scientific investigations take the form of a comparison of results obtained under two conditions, or with two kinds of material, as in the comparison of cigarette smokers and non-smokers, or worms intact and divided. What we want to know about are not two samples, but two populations. Therefore what we must compare are not two sample means, but two confidence intervals. Each confidence interval is a range of not-improbable values for a particular population mean. When the intervals overlap, how shall we calculate the proba-

bility that the mean of one population is really higher than
that of the other?

Is sclerosis of the aorta really accelerated in cigarette
smokers? Do divided worms really retain the effects of training as well as intact worms? When we try to answer questions
like these, on the basis of two samples in hand, it is like judg-
ing a wrestling match on the basis of one fall or betting on the
outcome of a football game from knowledge of the score after
the first quarter. The information may seem pretty conclusive
at some times, but at other times it is inconclusive or even misleading.

If we once get a clear idea of the problem, the solution is
not difficult. We are studying a difference, and therefore we
must view it as one member in a universe of differences. Let
us call the two sample means $\overline{X}$ and $\overline{Y}$. Each is a randomly
chosen member of its own universe. If we form all possible
pairs which include one member of each universe, we can use
these pairs to form either a universe of sums or a universe of
differences. We know, from the variance law, that for the universe of sums, the variance is equal to the sum of the variances
of the two sample universes; however, the differences can just
as well be regarded as sums, of the form $\overline{X} + (-\overline{Y})$, and it is
obvious that the variance of $-\overline{Y}$ values is exactly the same as
the variance of $\overline{Y}$ values. A change of sign does not influence
the scatter. So the same rule still holds: *the variance of a universe of differences is equal to the sum of the variances of the
separate universes from which the "members of the difference" have been drawn.* In symbols, referring specifically to
the difference between sample means:

$$\sigma_{\overline{X}-\overline{Y}}{}^2 = \sigma_{\overline{X}}{}^2 + \sigma_{\overline{Y}}{}^2.$$

To illustrate: if we consider all the possible pairs that might
be formed by catching 2 fish in a well-stocked pond and then
weighing them, the variance of weight-sums will be exactly

equal to the variance of weight-differences. But of course we must not make the Grand Duke's error, and ignore which fish was caught first. If sums and differences are formed by catching one bass from a lake and one trout from a stream, we must define whether the differences are to be taken as bass-minus-trout or as trout-minus-bass. The distributions will be dissimilar, but they will have the same mean difference and the same variance.

In terms of standard deviation, rather than of variance, the formula becomes:

$$\sigma_{\bar{X}-\bar{Y}} = \sqrt{\sigma_{\bar{X}}^2 + \sigma_{\bar{Y}}^2}.$$

This is called the *standard error of the difference*. If an experiment has significance, in a statistical sense, it is because the observed difference between sample means so far exceeds the standard error of that difference that it is possible to state with confidence, "That's no accident." The investigator has found what he was looking for: something highly improbable, under the conditions of the null hypothesis.

Please do not ever forget that there is a plus sign, not a minus sign, joining the two sample values for the variance of means. If your intuition balks at accepting this, a good way to persuade it is to conduct an empirical demonstration. Stock your own pond of bass and your own stream of trout. You can make the fish any size you please. For example, take 5 bass, weighing 2, 3, 3, 5, and 6 pounds. Take 4 trout, weighing 1, 2, 2, and 3 pounds. Now you must form 20 pairs and from each pair both a sum and a difference. Calculate the variances if you wish, but your intuition should give in as soon as the two distributions are set down side by side, one spreading as wide as the other. (You can see at once that the range of sums will be from 3 to 9, and the range of bass-minus-trout differences, from −1 to 5, while that for trout-minus-bass differences is from −5 to 1. Each range is 6, because the range of weights for bass was 4 pounds and for trout, 2 pounds. The variances will match just as neatly.)

To illustrate how the standard error of the difference is applied, we shall look first at some heart-moving statistics, from a recent study of how chickens adjust their blood circulation to seasonal changes in temperature. The investigators found that the average quantity of blood moved by a single heart beat is 1.20 milliliters in August, but 1.50 milliliters in chilly February.* In each case, the standard error was .06 milliliters. Thus the difference between the means is .30, and the standard error of the difference is $\sqrt{2(.06)^2}$, which is .085.

We call such a result significant, in a statistical sense, if there is not more than 1 chance in 20 that a contrary result (that is, a higher mean value for August than for February) would occur in a repetition of the experiment. The decision on this point is based on the ratio of the difference between the means to the standard error of the difference. Roughly speaking, any normally distributed statistic which is more than twice its standard error is an unlikely result of random sampling. More precisely, standard scores outside the limits $\pm 1.96\sigma$ occur by chance only 5 times in 100 in a normal distribution; those outside the range $\pm 2.58\sigma$ occur only 1 time in 100. (Using small-sample methods, the critical ratios are somewhat higher.) In this case, the ratio of the observed difference to its standard error equals $.30/.085 = 3.54$. This is a ratio which would not happen 1 time in 100 by chance. It seems reasonably certain, therefore, that chickens adjust to the demands of winter weather, in part, by increasing the average amplitude of each heart beat.

For further illustration, we present Table 12-1, which shows the results obtained by two physiologists, B. Coleman and V.

* James A. Vogel and Paul D. Sturkie, "Cardiovascular Responses of the Chicken to Seasonal and Induced Temperature Changes," *Science,* 140 (1963), 1404–1406.

TABLE 12-1. Application of the test for significance of a difference between means. Comparisons of epinephrine and norepinephrine content in various tissues of normal (control) rabbits and rabbits in which shock had been induced by hemorrhage. Means and standard errors are in micrograms per gram of tissue, with the number of observations in parenthesis. The final entry on each row is the probability that the observed difference might be a chance result. (< and > are read, respectively, as "less than" and "greater than.")

	COMPARISON OF EPINEPHRINE LEVELS		
Organ	*Control Animals*	*Shocked Animals*	*P*
Heart	.14 ± .06 (12)	.24 ± .06 (12)	>.05
Spleen	.08 ± .03 (12)	.36 ± .05 (4)	<.01
Brain	.02 ± .009 (20)	.12 ± .05 (13)	<.025
Liver	.07 ± .026 (14)	.23 ± .07 (12)	<.025
Muscle	.02 ± .027 (13)	.06 ± .04 (13)	>.30
	COMPARISON OF NOREPINEPHRINE LEVELS		
Organ	*Control Animals*	*Shocked Animals*	*P*
Heart	1.05 ± .13 (12)	.16 ± .05 (12)	<.001
Spleen	.49 ± .10 (10)	.00 (4)	<.001
Brain	.32 ± .04 (20)	.10 ± .04 (13)	<.01
Liver	.19 ± .05 (12)	.06 ± .03 (12)	<.05
Muscle	.19 ± .05 (12)	.10 ± .03 (13)	>.27

Source: B. Coleman and V. V. Glaviano, "Tissue Levels of Norepinephrine and Epinephrine in Hemorrhagic Shock," *Science*, 134 (1963), 54; with a correction provided by the authors.

V. Glaviano, who studied changes in the level of concentration of certain hormones, as a result of shock from loss of blood. Before looking at the results, let us say a few words about the role which these substances play in behavior. When an animal is frightened, increased amounts of epinephrine (also called adrenin, adrenaline) are released into the blood; conversely, if a large amount of epinephrine is injected into the blood stream, it will cause increased heart rate, rapid breathing, wide eyes, and other body changes which, taken together, give the picture of fear. In a man, these changes are usually accompanied by the feeling of fear. Norepinephrine is a closely related chemical, which occurs as a stage in the synthesis of epinephrine in the body. However, the injection of norepinephrine results in body changes—partly identical—which correspond to the picture of anger rather than fear. It has been reported that lions are relatively rich in norepinephrine, while deer and other passive animals which survive by flight rather than by attack are relatively rich in epinephrine. It has also been reported that people who tend to get angry easily have higher norepinephrine levels, and lower epinephrine levels, than those who tend to frighten easily. Knowing all this, would you care to guess about what would happen to an animal which is suffering a serious loss of blood?

Coleman and Glaviano, using delicate biochemical methods, measured the epinephrine and norepinephrine content in various body organs. In their experimental animals, they induced serious hemorrhages; the control animals were surgically handled in the same way, except that no hemorrhages were induced. Table 12-1 (which is slightly modified from the form in which it appeared in the original report) gives means and standard errors for each kind of measurement in each of the organs studied and also the number of measurements used to arrive at each mean. This complete reporting of results enables any reader to check the probability statements, which indicate whether the differences between control and experimental animals can be regarded as random samples from the same universe. Let us review the calculation of one of these probabilities.

Taking mean values for norepinephrine in the liver, the animals in shock show a lower level than the controls. For the difference between means, we have

$$.19 - .06 = .13.$$

For the standard error of the difference, we have

$$\sqrt{.05^2 + .03^2} = .0583.$$

The ratio, .13/.0583, equals 2.23. This surpasses the critical value for significant probability, and we therefore conclude that the result is significant, because it would occur less than 5 times in 100 by chance. (The result is the same using small-sample methods, which, in this case, require a critical ratio of 2.07, instead of 1.96.) All other probability values in Table 12-1 have been similarly calculated.

Chapter 13

HOW TO TELL
A MISFIT

●

A PROBABILITY DISTRIBUTION is only a mathematical toy until someone shows that it "fits" a class of events. After that, it is a tool of science. However, nature seems to have anticipated every complexity that a mathematician can imagine, and the chance is good that any curve whatever will find its place somewhere, sometime, in the jigsaw puzzle of real events.

When Pascal turned deeply religious toward the end of his too-short life, he regretted the labors he had expended in solving the riddles which had been posed by his gaming friends. Staring into eternity, he felt that his former preoccupation with mathematics had been almost as frivolous as their concern over a purse of gold. Surely, he would have been less remorseful if he could have foreseen that some day his method of combinatorial analysis, giving rise to the binomial distribution of probabilities, would become the indispensable tool of a new science—genetics. Because the binomial distribution corresponds to the distribution of inherited traits under certain circumstances, the geneticist is able to verify his hypotheses by comparing actual physical characteristics (of men, or plants, or fruit flies) with calculated theoretical expectations.

Two centuries later, practical applications of probability theory were still rare. Poisson could not guess that the distribution which he devised in connection with his speculations about the administration of justice in the criminal courts would some day be used by Rutherford and Geiger to show that the discharge of alpha particles from a radioactive disk is regulated by chance. Since then, the same distribution has found innumerable other scientific and technological applications.

Augustin Louis Cauchy (1789–1857) could not guess that the strange distribution which bears his name—a symmetrical distribution which has neither a determinable mean nor a finite variance—would be used a century later to describe the scatter and capture of particles by atomic nuclei. Poisson and Cauchy were both outstanding theoretical physicists of their day, but it would have taken more than human genius to anticipate how these "offbeat" contributions to the theory of probability would find their place in the physics of the twentieth century.

For the scientific application of probability, we need some objective way to decide when a theoretical distribution really does fit a set of events. It is not enough simply to assert, as Quetelet did, for example, that all human traits are distributed as errors of nature, whose "aim" is to produce the perfect or average man, and that therefore they must be normally distributed. However, Quetelet was on the right track. He devised a cumbersome way to fit data to a normal distribution, and Francis Galton subsequently used Quetelet's method to set up his "classification of men according to their natural gifts." But they had no objective way to test whether such an assumption was justified. All they could do was to look at the discrepancies and make a subjective judgment as to whether the fit looked good or bad. Since there is no experience which is free of error, we can never expect a really snug fit, and a loose fit leaves room for personal prejudice to sway our judgment one way or another.

The general statistical approach to this problem is clear enough. The theoretical distribution is a universe, and the empirical observations are a sample. We must ask the question: what is the probability that this sample might have come from that universe by chance? We speak of good fit if the probability is high, and poor fit if it is low.

We start, therefore, by placing the observed frequencies, based on actual experience, side by side with theoretical frequencies which are calculated from a probability distribution. This has been done, in Table 13-1, for the little sampling experiment of Chapter 3, in which we counted odd and even digits in groups of five (calling them "heads" and "tails") in a table of random digits. The results of that sampling process are the observed frequencies (headed f_o) in Table 13-1. Ac-

TABLE 13-1. Computation of chi square, the index of discrepancy, for observed and expected frequencies in a sampling experiment.

X	f_o	f_e	$|f_o - f_e|$	$\dfrac{(f_o - f_e)^2}{f_e}$
5	11	10	1	.10
4	49	50	1	.02
3	112	100	12	1.44
2	91	100	9	.81
1	46	50	4	.32
0	11	10	1	.10
	320	320		2.79*

* With 5 degrees of freedom, chi square must exceed 11.07 to indicate significant departure from the theoretical expectation. (See Table 13-2.)

cording to theory, they should follow the binomial distribution for $N = 5$ and $p = \frac{1}{2}$. Therefore the theoretical or expected frequencies (headed f_e) are numbers taken from the

Pascal triangle, multiplied by a factor which makes their sum equal to the sum of observed frequencies.

The next and very obvious step is to look at the differences or discrepancies between these two columns of figures. They are entered in the column of absolute discrepancies (headed $|f_o - f_e|$). Naturally enough, these differences tend to be small in classes which have small theoretical frequencies; that is, they vary partly as a function of the size of the theoretical frequency. Of course it will be necessary to take this circumstance into account in constructing an index of discrepancy.

In the last column, each entry is the square of the discrepancy, divided by the expected frequency. Let us emphasize again, as in an earlier chapter, that these differences are not squared "to get rid of the minus signs." We have already done that simply by considering the differences as absolute magnitudes, and there is nothing evasive or antimathematical about such a maneuver. We use squares because they give us a better clue to cause–effect relationships, just as we divide by the expected frequency because this, too, helps to give each discrepancy its proper weight in the final accounting. After these two adjustments, we add the results.

The sum of these squared and proportioned discrepancies is called χ^2, chi square. The definition of chi square is a symbolic statement of the operations we have just described:

$$\chi^2 = \Sigma \frac{(f_o - f_e)^2}{f_e}.$$

This serves as an *index of discrepancy* which can be used to judge *goodness of fit*. However, before it can be put to that use, we must know the probability distribution for such a sum. As a matter of fact, the sum in this instance, 2.79, is one which does indicate good fit, because more often than not, under similar circumstances, we would get a value greater than this by chance. But we shall have to discuss the chi-square distributions in order to see why this is so.

THE CHI-SQUARE DISTRIBUTIONS

Karl Pearson showed that the index of discrepancy which is calculated by this procedure is distributed approximately in the same manner as the sum of squares for a random sample of standard scores from a normal distribution. Let us see what this means.

Start with a normal distribution. Change all the scores into standard scores. (That is, divide each one by the standard deviation.) The resulting distribution has a mean equal to 0 and a standard deviation (as well as a mean square) equal to 1. Now square every score in that distribution. We may dismiss the negative scores from consideration, since they are all rendered positive by squaring. Of the positive scores, those which are less than 1 become smaller, and very small values become increasingly frequent. For example, 0.5 becomes 0.25, and 0.1 becomes 0.01. In fact, the pile-up of very small values is so great that we can set no bounds to it, and we merely say that the frequency gets higher and higher without limit as we approach the limiting score of zero. The larger values, on the contrary, are increased by squaring: 2 becomes 4, 3 becomes 9, and so on. So, while the *probability density* becomes greater and greater for smaller and smaller scores, it becomes less and less for larger and larger scores. The mean obviously is 1, because this is the distribution of squares from a standardized distribution in which the mean square must be 1.

This is called the chi-square distribution with 1 degree of freedom. We shall use it as a sort of grab bag from which to draw random samples. The distribution of sums, for a universe of samples containing any stated number of scores randomly chosen from this parent population, is called the chi-square distribution with so many *degrees of freedom* (*df*). (See Figure 6.)

When *df* is a small number, the chi-square distributions still have a strong skew, because most members in the parent population are small. As *df* grows larger the skew becomes less pronounced, until the distributions are almost normal after *df* reaches about 30. They are never quite normal, for in each of

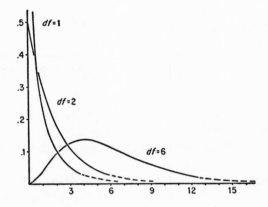

FIGURE 6. Three chi-square distributions. In each, 95 per cent of the probability surface lies beneath the solid line, and 1 per cent, beyond the end of the broken line.

these distributions the expected value equals *df* and the modal value equals *df* − 2. (The distribution for *df* = 1 has no determinable mode, since it approaches 0 as an asymptote.) We shall not face up to the very complicated formula by which probabilities are calculated in chi-square distributions. Fortunately, it is not necessary to use the formula in order to apply the method. All that is needed is a table of critical values.

Table 13-2 gives values of chi square which are exceeded 5 times in 100 and 1 time in 100, when there are not more

TABLE 13-2. Critical values of chi square, when degrees of freedom do not exceed 10. The probabilities are for values equal to or greater than those shown. For any chi-square distribution, $P = .5$ for values greater than $df-2$, where df represents the number of degrees of freedom.

df	$P = .05$	$P = .01$	df	$P = .05$	$P = .01$
1	3.841	6.635	6	12.592	16.812
2	5.991	9.210	7	14.067	18.475
3	7.815	11.345	8	15.507	20.090
4	9.488	13.277	9	16.919	21.666
5	11.070	15.086	10	18.307	23.299

Source: Abridged from Table III of Ronald A. Fisher, *Statistical Methods for Research Workers,* published by Oliver & Boyd, Ltd., Edinburgh, by permission of the publishers.

than 10 degrees of freedom. The entries for $df = 1$ are, of course, simply the squares of 1.96 and 2.58, values with which we are already familiar as critical points in the normal distribution.

One thing remains before we can perform a test of fit: we must know how to select the appropriate chi-square distribution for a particular problem. Let us look again at Table 13-1. The chi-square value there is made up of six parts, each of which is based on a comparison between an observed and an expected frequency. At first glance, therefore, one might suppose that the correct distribution to use is the one which results from adding six squared randomly selected normal deviates. However, that would be the case only if the six choices were independent, that is, if there were really six separate tests of the hypothesis that the two series of frequencies agree. As a matter of fact, the comparisons on the various rows are not independent, because the two sets of frequencies have been forced to agree in one respect: both have the same total. Consequently, if one entry were missing from either column, you could fill it in just by looking at the total of the other column. The mathematician describes this situation by saying that it has only 5 degrees of freedom. Therefore the result is to be judged by the critical values of the chi-square distribution for 5 degrees of freedom.

The general rule which governs all tests of fit, whenever comparison is made between observed and expected frequencies, is that there are as many degrees of freedom as the number of comparisons *less* the number of ways in which the two sets of frequencies have been forced to agree. Whenever a value taken from the observations is used as a basis for calculating the expected frequencies, one degree of freedom is lost. In this problem, only the total was used in that way.

Let us now make another test of fit to a binomial distribution, under somewhat different circumstances. Table 13-3

TABLE 13-3. Test of fit for Geissler's data on the distribution of male births in families with 8 children.

BOYS	OBSERVED FAMILIES	EXPECTED FAMILIES	$\dfrac{(f_o-f_e)^2}{f_e}$
8	342	264.3	22.84
7	2,092	1,993.8	4.84
6	6,678	6,580.2	1.45
5	11,929	12,409.9	18.63
4	14,959	14,627.6	7.51
3	10,649	11,034.7	13.48
2	5,331	5,202.6	3.17
1	1,485	1,401.7	4.95
0	215	165.2	15.00
	53,680	53,680.0	91.87*

Source: Adapted from Table 11 of Ronald A. Fisher, *Statistical Methods for Research Workers,* published by Oliver & Boyd, Ltd., Edinburgh, by permission of the publishers.
* With 7 degrees of freedom, chi square in excess of 18.475 indicates less than 1 chance in 100 of only chance departure from the theoretical expectation.

reports observations on the number of male births in families with 8 children. However, expected frequencies are not based on the assumption that male and female births should be equally likely. In these empirical observations, there are about 18 boys to every 17 girls, and the calculation of expected frequencies is based on that fact. Since two empirically based values have been used (p and N), two rows might be left blank in either column, and filled in from a knowledge of those values. (The total of both entries must be just enough to make the correct number of families, and it must be divided among the two cells in a way that would produce the required proportion of boys for the entire distribution.) Therefore there are only 7 degrees of freedom in the test of fit, although there are 9 classes available for comparison.

In this case, the high value of chi square indicates that the fit is poor, and therefore we conclude that the sex of a child is not quite a chance matter and that parents do differ in their tendency to produce children of one sex rather than another. Whatever nonchance influence is present is slight enough, or rare enough, so that it is necessary to have this enormous aggregation of data in order to demonstrate it with assurance. If the same proportional distribution of the sexes had been found in about 5,000 families, each with 8 children, it would not be possible to reject the hypothesis of binomial fit.

This draws our attention to an important point: chi square is influenced by the quantity of data as well as by the proportionate distribution of scores. A large value of chi square indicates a nonchance result, but, as in this case, it does not necessarily mean that the discrepancy is large in the proportionate sense.

The test of fit to a Poisson distribution involves a loss of two degrees of freedom, unless the mean value is fixed by some purely theoretical consideration. Table 8-6 compares observed and expected frequencies of mitoses. The calculation of the expected values is based on the fact that 4.2 mitoses is the mean number observed in each grid square. The last column of the table carries out the test of fit, which leads to the conclusion that mitoses are distributed through the tissue sample in a random manner. Although there are 8 classes available for comparison (after merging certain classes to avoid any very small expected frequencies, a possible source of misleading results), there are only 6 degrees of freedom. The result, $\chi^2 = 6.25$, is well below the critical value for that distribution, and therefore it indicates merely chance discrepancy.

The test of fit for a normal distribution involves a little more computational work, but it is not different in principle. Usually 3 degrees of freedom are lost, because the expected frequencies are based on a mean, a standard deviation, and a number taken from the observed data. That would be the case whenever the question posed was simply whether certain data are to be regarded as a random sample from a normal distribution. However, if we were to test the hypothesis that the distribution of intelligence test scores in a certain community corresponds to the national distribution, we might use the mean and standard deviation based on national experience, and then only 1 degree of freedom would be lost. The underlying principle is always the same: the degrees of freedom are equal to the number of classes available for comparison less the number of ways in which the two series of frequencies have been forced to agree.

Chapter 14

ANOTHER SIGN
OF INDEPENDENCE

•

THE CHI SQUARE TECHNIQUE is so flexible that it often plays the part of a statistical first aid kit, which can be used to meet any emergency. The most common use of chi square is not for tests of good fit, where it is irreplaceable, but for what are called tests of independence, where it provides a quick and easy substitute for more elaborate methods.

In a test of good fit, we compare a set of observations with a set of expectations based on some prior assumptions about how they should have turned out. In most investigations, we compare two or more sets of observations made under differing conditions, leaving our expectations aside. The test of fit asks whether a sample might have come, by chance, from a certain kind of universe. The test of independence asks whether two or more samples belong to the same universe, without making any prior assumptions about the nature of that universe. We take samples from two populations (men and women, for example, or Democrats and Republicans), and, having found them to differ (in their opinions about television programs, for example), we ask whether this difference might have happened by chance. Better stated: we assert that the difference happened by chance in random sampling from one universe. This is the null hypothesis, or hypothesis of independence, which we must put to the test.

For any comparison of this sort, the observations must be classified in two ways. First, there is the classification by groups or treatments and, second, the classification by results or scores. The null hypothesis is put in the form of a hypothesis of independence: that regardless of which group we consider, the probability of a given score remains the same.

The simplest use of chi square is for a test of independence in a two-by-two classification. In such a table, the "scores" are simple dichotomies, such as "yes" and "no" or "above the median" and "below the median." You will recall that we performed such a test in Chapter 5, comparing monkeys which had been either "stressed" or (as controls) "nonstressed" as to whether they "died" or "survived." At that time, we used an exact test based on binomial probabilities, which would be inconvenient with larger numbers. Conversely, the chi-square test is often insufficiently accurate with numbers as small as in that experiment. (In that particular case, as it happens, it would lead to a very similar result, but one will not always be so fortunate.)

More suitable material to demonstrate the use of chi square for a test of independence in a fourfold table is provided by an investigation which we discussed in Chapter 7 and which dealt with changes in the spontaneous rate of discharge of neurons in the brain. You will recall that, in the waking state, as compared to the sleeping state, the mean rate of discharge increased, but the median rate decreased. (See Table 7-2.) The original data can also be classified according to (1) whether the discharge rate for a given neuron is above or below the median during sleep and (2) whether it increases or decreases on awakening. The results of this new two-by-two classification are given in Table 14-1. The two systems of classification do not seem to be independent, because there is

TABLE 14-1. Ninety neurons in the visual cortex of cats, classified according to whether the spontaneous rate of discharge is (1) above or below the median rate, during sleep, and (2) faster or slower awake than asleep. Numbers in parentheses are expected frequencies based on the hypothesis of independence.

	FASTER AWAKE	FASTER ASLEEP	TOTALS
Sleep-rate above median	27 (21)	18 (24)	45
Sleep-rate below median	15 (21)	30 (24)	45
TOTALS	42	48	90

$\chi^2 = 6.43$; $P < .05$.

Source: E. V. Evarts, E. Bental, B. Bihari, and P. R. Huttenlocher, "Spontaneous Discharge of Single Neurons during Sleep and Waking," *Science*, 135 (1962), 726–728.

a tendency for neurons which have a higher spontaneous rate during sleep to increase this rate, rather than decrease it, on awakening. On the other hand, those with a lower spontaneous rate during sleep tend to become still slower on awakening. We want to test whether this disproportion can be considered a chance result.

Under the hypothesis of independence, if a certain proportion of the neurons with "sleep-rate above the median" increase their rate of discharge when the cat awakes, the same proportion of neurons with "sleep-rate below the median" should do the same. If they do not (and, of course, in these observations they do not), only chance is to be held responsible.

Expected frequencies are calculated solely on the basis of the observations, using the proportions found in the marginal totals to represent those in the universe. One might say that the marginal totals *are* the hypothesis, since by their help we calculate expected frequencies which stand in the same proportion, row by row in each column, column by column in each row. Each expected frequency is calculated by multiplying its row sum and its column sum and dividing by the total for the table:

$$f_e = \frac{n_R \, n_C}{n}.$$

Once the expected frequencies have been calculated, the question of independence reduces to a question of good fit. We compare the observed and expected frequencies, just as we did in Chapter 13. Using the same formula, we square each discrepancy, divide by the corresponding expected frequency, and then add. In this case, we find that chi square equals 6.43, and, since there is only 1 degree of freedom, the hypothesis that the two systems of classification are independent must be rejected.

Exactly the same method can be used for larger contingency tables, which are based on more complex systems of classification. To illustrate this, we shall reconsider the data of Table 9-3, giving grade-point averages for male college students classified according to their smoking habits. In order to construct a workable contingency table from these data, we shall classify the students as having grade-point averages 2.5 and above, 2.00–2.49, and below 2.00. (These divisions are not arbitrary; having decided that the largest workable number of classes on this scale would be 3—because expected values below 5 in any cell are to be avoided if possible—the entire population was divided into three parts as equal as the already existing classification would permit.) This gives rise to the following table of observed frequencies:

GRADE POINTS	NON-SMOKERS	LIGHT	MODERATE	HEAVY
Above 2.49	44	9	10	5
2.00–2.49	28	8	19	11
Below 2.00	15	11	22	5

Using the marginal sums (which are not shown), expected frequencies are calculated. As before, each expected frequency is the product of row-sum and column-sum divided by the number in the table. The result:

GRADE POINTS	NON-SMOKERS	LIGHT	MODERATE	HEAVY
Above 2.49	31.6	10.2	18.6	7.6
2.00–2.49	30.7	9.9	18.0	7.4
Below 2.00	24.7	7.9	14.4	6.0

Now, still following the same procedure as for the two-by-two table, the value of $(f_o - f_e)^2/f_e$ is calculated separately for each cell. In the first cell, for example, we calculate $(44-31.6)^2/31.6 = 4.88$. It is worthwhile to write these values also into a similar table:

GRADE POINTS	NON-SMOKERS	LIGHT	MODERATE	HEAVY
Above 2.49	4.88	.14	3.98	.89
2.00–2.49	.24	.37	.06	1.75
Below 2.00	3.82	1.22	2.16	.17
Totals	8.94	1.73	6.20	2.81
				(19.68)

To determine the number of degrees of freedom, we reason as follows: there are twelve comparisons of observed and expected frequencies, but only six of these can be made "without constraint." Fill in two rows in three columns, and all the other entries (one in each row and column) can be written down from a knowledge of the marginal sums, which must be the same for observed and expected values. We shall discuss this question of degrees of freedom a little more fully later, but for the present let this principle guide us in deciding that the table has 6 degrees of freedom. Therefore (referring to Table 13-2), the result would not happen one time in 100 by chance.

The cell-by-cell distribution of values which have gone into this chi-square total tells us that the result is due primarily to the fact that, among the nonsmokers, there is a greater-than-expected proportion of good students and a less-than-expected proportion of poor students.

Let us return to the question of degrees of freedom. The data of a two-by-two table represent a single test of the hypothesis that the two systems of classification are independent. If additional tests are made, they can be represented in other similar tables, or they can be combined into a larger contingency table. In fact, any larger contingency table can be broken down into a series of independent tests of the same null hypothesis, that is, the hypothesis that all the samples are randomly drawn from the same universe. This is a needlessly involved way to go about deciding how many degrees of freedom exist in the table, but it is worthwhile to consider how this might be done, in order to get a better understanding of the meaning of degrees of freedom and to recognize that chi square computed from such a table is really a sum of as many chi squares as there are degrees of freedom.

In this case, it is possible to break the data down into six independent fourfold tables, each of which represents a separate and independent test of the question whether smoking habits and grade-point averages are related. There is more than one possible series of such tests, but here is one way it might be done:

Nonsmokers versus light smokers
    (a) Above 2.49 versus below 2.50
    (b) 2.00–2.49 versus below 2.00
Moderate versus heavy smokers
    (a) and (b) as above
Nonsmokers and light smokers versus heavy and
      moderate smokers
    (a) and (b) as above

Construct the six two-by-two tables indicated by this schedule. Satisfy yourself that they are really independent, that is, that the results in one do not in any way influence the result in any other. Satisfy yourself, also, that it is not possible to arrange a seventh table which will be independent of these six. Then calculate chi square for each one, and you will find that the total will differ very little from the total we found for the table treated as a whole. This demonstrates the real meaning of the concept of degrees of freedom in such a situation.

Table 14-2 presents the data of a basically similar investigation dealing with a much more serious effect of smoking. The purpose of this investigation was to determine the influence of smoking habits on the sclerosis or hardening of the aorta which frequently leads to serious forms of heart disease. The data come from a long series of autopsies made at a Veterans Administration hospital, on bodies of persons who had died from many causes. In each autopsy, the appearance of the aorta was compared to a series of photographic transparencies, and in this way a "sclerotic age" was assigned. If this age was fixed at more than ten years over the chronological age of the deceased, the case was classified as having "above-average sclerosis"; if at more than ten years below the chronological age, then as having "below-average sclerosis." Each case was also classified according to smoking habits, based on clinical histories.

The same series of calculations which has been set forth in detail for the preceding illustration lead in this case to a chi square of 48.14. With 8 degrees of freedom, this is significant at the 1 per-cent level. In other words, smoking habits are shown to be related to the development of sclerosis of the aorta, which is a kind of premature aging. Analysis of the table shows, however, that pipe- and cigar-smokers have fared no worse than nonsmokers. Furthermore, the aorta is not directly exposed to the effects of smoke, as are the lungs.

One must always remember that the demonstration of a

TABLE 14–2. Classification of 870 autopsies according to severity of aortic sclerosis and smoking habits, with calculation of the index of discrepancy, chi square. Frequencies reconstructed from percentages in the original report, where the statistical treatment follows a different plan.

SCLEROSIS	NON-SMOKERS	HEAVY CIGARETTE	MODERATE CIGARETTE	LIGHT CIGARETTE	PIPE AND CIGAR	TOTALS
Observed Frequencies						
Above average	16	50	76	29	7	178
Average	97	122	180	96	42	537
Below average	48	27	32	27	21	155
TOTALS	161	199	288	152	70	870
Expected, on the hypothesis of independence						
Above average	32.9	40.7	58.9	31.1	14.3	177.9
Average	99.4	122.8	177.8	93.8	43.2	537
Below average	28.7	35.4	51.3	27.1	12.5	155
TOTALS	161	198.9	288	152	70	869.9
$(f_o-f_e)^2/f_e$						
Above average	8.68	2.13	4.96	.14	3.73	19.64
Average	.06	.01	.03	.05	.03	.18
Below average	12.98	1.99	7.57	.00	5.78	28.32
TOTALS	21.72	4.13	12.56	.19	9.54	48.14

$\chi^2 = 48.14$; $df = 8$; $P < .01$

Source: S. L. Wilens and C. M. Plair, "Cigarette Smoking and Arteriosclerosis," *Science,* 138 (1962), 975–977, p. 976.

statistical dependence does not prove a direct causal connection. On the other hand, it does demonstrate that some causal link, however indirect, exists. This is a problem with which we shall deal more thoroughly in Chapter 15. That chapter must also deal with the problem of the strength of an association, as distinguished from the certainty that an association exists.

Chapter 15

CAUSE OR
CIRCUMSTANCE?

●

THE PROPRIETOR of a shoe store ordered three dozen pair of sandals from a manufacturer. He asked that two dozen be of medium size, with half a dozen each of large and small. The shipment arrived in two boxes, of which one contained 36 sandals for the left foot, while the other contained an equal number for the right foot. Being busy with other things, he asked a clerk to put the sandals into stock boxes, in pairs. However, he neglected to mention that the sandals were of different sizes, and the clerk created "random" pairs which were distributed approximately like this:

	Small right	Medium right	Large right
Large left	1	4	1
Medium left	4	16	4
Small left	1	4	1

So the shopkeeper had him do the job over again. The young man may have been careless, or he may have been dis-

The World of Probability

tracted, or he may have had very poor perception of size differences. Probably all of these factors played their part in producing this result:

	Small right	Medium right	Large right
Large left	0	3	3
Medium left	3	18	3
Small left	3	3	0

Finally, the shopkeeper did the job himself. When he had finished, the sandals were assorted like this:

	Small right	Medium right	Large right
Large left	0	0	6
Medium left	0	24	0
Small left	6	0	0

The first table contains no evidence of functional relationship between left and right sizes. In the second table a functional relationship is evident, but it is confused by chance, that is, some influences other than the functional relationship between the left and right sizes are helping to form the pairs. In the third table, the pairing of sandals is determined solely by the functional relationship.

There are many phenomena which, being studied in pairs, reveal functional relationships. Here is an example: the size of the mackerel catch by British fishing vessels, during May, has yearly ups and downs according to the number of days of sunshine in the fishing area during the previous February and March. In this case, the pairs are formed by taking together the weather records and the fishing records for the same year.*

* E. J. Allen, "Mackerel and Sunshine," *Journal of the Marine Biological Association of the United Kingdom*, 8 (1909), 394–406.

It would be wrong to conclude that the mackerel thrive on sunshine. As a matter of fact, until late in April they are swimming in other seas. The explanation seems to be that more sunshine leads to a greater abundance of phytoplankton (plant organisms in the water), which in turn leads to a richer development of zooplankton (tiny animal organisms), which in due course attracts larger numbers of mackerel. (This in turn attracts larger numbers of fishing vessels.) Demonstrating a statistical association is only the first step toward the discovery of causal relationships, but it is frequently a very important one.

As another example, consider the debate over whether cigarette smoking is a "cause" of lung cancer. The conclusion that it is rests primarily on evidence similar to some that we reviewed in Chapter 14, dealing with the association between smoking habits and academic grades, or with sclerosis of the aorta. Certainly smoking does not "cause" poor grades. Therefore some persons deny, likewise, that there is any real proof of causal relationship between smoking and cancer, asserting that the evidence must be regarded as "merely circumstantial" until someone explains how cigarette smoking causes cancer. But then, neither can a physicist explain how one billiard ball imparts its motion to another, and no one doubts the causal relationship. One difference between these two cases is that for the billiard balls the effect is invariable, while in the other case the lethal outcome cannot be predicted in each individual instance, but only statistically, that is, for a certain proportion of all smokers. This does not mean that explanation is necessarily easier in one case than in the other. An invariable effect—such as the magnetic field set up by current flowing in a wire—may be difficult to understand, while an occasional effect—like fish biting on a baited hook—may have a fairly obvious explanation. The important difference is that the invariable effect has *one* determinant, while the uncertain event has many determinants. Complex biological and social phenomena are typically inconstant, because it is rarely possible to identify a single causal factor which leads to an invariable outcome. Nevertheless, the demonstration of statistical dependence is positive proof of some causal connection, however indirect. Often the two phenomena will be effects of some third phenomenon and do not influence each other, but in one way or another our search for explanation must take statistical dependence into account.

The pioneer in the statistical study of functional relationships was Francis Galton (1822–1911). Galton had a many-sided career in which he gained distinction as explorer, anthropologist, meteorologist, and psychologist. His motto was: "Whenever you can, count." Sitting at a lecture, he might count the coughs and fidgets of the audience, as a measure of their attentiveness. On his walks, he sometimes counted how many women he passed who were strikingly beautiful, ordinary, or plain, thus gathering materials for a "beauty map" of England. He was the first to prepare weather maps, and thus to discover that weather travels in anticyclones. He also developed the system for classification of fingerprints. In short, Galton was richly endowed with that type of genius which has been defined as "an infinite capacity for detail."

He is remembered best as the founder of eugenics. The storm which was stirred up when his cousin, Charles Darwin, published *The Origin of Species* (1859), raged mostly around the question of mankind's past, as an offshoot of "monkeys." Galton drew conclusions for the future. He reasoned that breeding better human beings is just as much the business of science as breeding better livestock. (Years later, in a letter to Karl Pearson, he described with satisfaction a *Punch* cartoon in which a nobleman addresses his prize bull: "By Jove, you are a fine fellow!" and receives the answer: "So would you have been, my Lord, if they had taken as much pains with your ancestors, as you did with mine.")

Galton was untiring in his efforts to demonstrate the influence of heredity on all physical and mental characteristics. He selected physical stature as an easily measurable trait which was especially suitable for his purpose, and it was his study of the relationship between the height of children and that of their parents which led to the concept of correlation, as a statistical measure of functional relationship. He assembled his data into charts similar to Table 15-1. (This particular chart is based on later work by Pearson.) In this chart, each entry stands for a *pair* of scores: the height of a father and that of his son. If, for each pair, you place a poker chip on the appropriate square, the piles of chips will form a mound with roughly elliptical contour lines. Any vertical or horizontal cross section through this mound—that is, any column or row—has the same general form as the corresponding marginal distribution, but a reduced range and variance. In these respects the chart closely resembles the second of the three tables introduced early in this chapter, in our little fable about the sandals.

Galton must have been disappointed because the correspondence in stature between fathers and sons was less strong than he had anticipated. He explained the result to his own satisfaction by supposing that a child has half his heredity from his two parents, a fourth from his four grandparents, an eighth from his great-grandparents, and so forth—or rather, and so backward. Since more remote ancestors, taken as a group, are likely to be more-or-less average, the result would be a tendency, in Galton's phrase, for "regression toward mediocrity." The word *regression* has won a permanent place in the vocabulary of statistics, although with a somewhat different meaning.

The effects which Galton attributed to remote ancestral heredity are, in one way or another, effects of chance. Sons tend to resemble their fathers (and brothers) because of common hereditary factors. They also differ from their fathers (and brothers) not only because of environmental influences,

TABLE 15-1. Stature of fathers (horizontal dimension) and sons (vertical dimension), in inches.

	58–59	60–61	62–63	64–65	66–67	68–69	70–71	72–73	74–75	Row Totals
78–79						1	1	1		3
76–77						3	2	4		9
74–75			1	1	2	10	12	8	3	37
72–73				4	11	32	35	21	2	105
70–71			1	17	50	76	65	23	4	236
68–69		2	15	38	90	106	53	17	1	322
66–67		5	16	53	87	53	21	3		238
64–65	3	3	12	35	30	12	5			100
62–63		1	5	7	9	2				24
60–61			1	2	1					4
TOTALS	3	11	51	157	279	296	194	77	10	1078

Source: Condensed from a table in K. Pearson and A. Lee, "On the Laws of Inheritance in Man," Biometrika, 2 (1902–1903), 415.

but because heredity itself includes chance elements. A single column in Table 15-1 consists of all the observations on sons whose fathers are of approximately the same height. Differences within the column are due to what Quetelet would have called "errors of Nature," which aims to give the same height to all sons of like fathers. The so-called regression problem is to select the best representative score for each column—the score which would be the best guess for the height of any son having such a father. We call this a *regressed score*.

If the estimate for each column had to be based solely on the observations recorded in that column, their mean would be the best guess, because that is the score which yields the smallest sum of squared deviations for the empirical scores in the column. But with the whole table to go on, it is possible to do better. One way to make use of the information in the other columns is to assume that there ought to be a consistent change from one column to the next. Obviously, it is a matter of chance that in this table, fathers who are 74 or 75 inches tall actually have sons who are shorter, on the average, than those of fathers who are only 72 or 73 inches tall. It is logical to "smooth out" such inconsistencies. If the functonal relationship is the same throughout the table, the best guesses for all the columns should fall on a straight line. So we assume they do, unless the column means are so far from being in a straight line that it is not reasonable to suppose that the discrepancies are wholly due to chance.

This so-called *regression line* will express the strength of the relationship between the two variables in the table. The greater the differences between the regressed scores, the steeper must be the regression line which connects them. Actually there are two regression lines, since the functional relationship is a reciprocal matter. We not only guess that a short father will have a short son, but with equal logic we guess that a short son probably had a short father. However, if it is true that the functional relationship is consistent through-

out the table, then these two lines have a symmetrical relationship to each other.

Galton himself never got much beyond this general approach. It was Karl Pearson who recognized—almost twenty
years after Galton had first wrestled with the problem—that
the solution had been given fifty years earlier by a French
astronomer, A. Bravais, in an article dealing with errors in
the location of a point in space. His formula, for what is now
called Pearson's product-moment coefficient of correlation, is
surprisingly simple. If all the individual scores have been converted into standard scores, the slope of the regression line,
r, is equal to the mean product obtained from the two scores
of each pair. Or one may use ordinary deviation scores and
add a standardization factor to the formula, thus:

$$ r = \frac{\Sigma\{x_i y_i\}}{n} \cdot \frac{1}{\sigma_X \, \sigma_Y} \, . $$

When regressed scores are fixed in this way, the sum of
within-column squared deviations will be larger, indeed, than
the sum of squares from the column mean, but the sum
of such squares for the entire table will be smaller than
for any other straight-line set of regressed scores. (See Appendix F.)

If you study this formula, you will see that whenever there
is perfect agreement between the two series of scores—in this
example, between the height of each father and his son—the
mean product of paired scores will be the same thing as the
mean square of either series, since either way, scores are
being multiplied by themselves. Therefore the highest value
which *r* can ever reach is the mean square of a standard distribution, which is 1. If there is a perfect inverse correspondence, so that the tallest father has the shortest son, and vice
versa, the value of *r* would be − 1. If the pairs are formed

purely by chance assortment, the coefficient of correlation will of course differ from 0 only by chance.

By this formula, the correlation coefficient for the table we have been studying equals .51. The size of this coefficient expresses the fact that as fathers grow taller inch by inch, their sons grow taller half-inch by half-inch. It also means that if you convert a father's height into a standard score, the best guess for his son's height is one-half that score. This merely restates what the regression line shows geometrically, as it rises approximately half a unit for each full unit of movement from left to right across the chart. Fathers also grow taller half-inch by half-inch, on the average, as their sons grow taller inch by inch! This is not surprising, because they have as much in common with their sons as their sons have in common with them. As stated earlier, the mathematical equivalence of the two regression lines is a consequence of the assumption that whatever functional relationship exists is consistent throughout the table. When that assumption is not valid, r is not a proper measure of the functional relationship. (We shall return to this point shortly.)

Correlation coefficients of approximately .50 have repeatedly been obtained not only for parent–child resemblance in physical traits, but also for such resemblance among brothers, or in brother–sister pairs. Correlations of the same size are typically found for parent–child resemblance, or resemblance among children of the same parents, in tests of intelligence. It should be remembered that a good many genes go into the determination of stature, as well as intelligence, and the similarity of genetic make-up between one parent and his child is just about the same as between sisters and brothers. Correlations between identical twins are invariably higher, because they have the same genetic constitution. Although studies of intrafamilial correlations often leave some uncertainty about the relative importance of heredity and environment in determining the particular trait being measured, the significantly higher correlation obtained between identical twins, compared with nonidentical twins, usually provides convincing demonstration of the importance of heredity. In a study of bone development, for example, E. L. Reynolds found correlations of .71 between identical twins, .28 between brothers, .12 between first cousins, and −.01 between unrelated individuals.

As an example of the use of correlation in economics, we may cite a study of the rate of migration from the rural prefectures of Japan to the great metropolitan areas. Minoru Tachi calculated a "relative migration potential" for each prefecture, based on the real per capita income relative to the national average, and he found that the correlation between this index and the actual net migration was .86 for the five-year period 1950–1955 and .92 for the period 1955–1960.* This does not mean that everyone who leaves a rural prefecture for Tokyo or Osaka does so because he is looking for a better job, but there is a clear causal relationship between the general level of income and the varied factors which induce different persons to migrate to the cities. The phenomenon may not be too different from the migration of mackerel into the Irish Sea.

One interesting application of correlation is to forecast achievement on the basis of so-called aptitude tests. For example, if past experience shows that there is a correlation between scores on a certain test and success in a school of dentistry, that test can be used for selecting entrants to the school, or advising would-be dentists. However, it is important to remember that "regression" is always toward the average—downward for those who had scores above the mean on the test, but upward for those whose test scores were below the mean. This is because even the best test only samples the

* Minoru Tachi, "Regional Income Disparity and Internal Migration of Population in Japan, *Economic Development and Cultural Change,* XII (1964), 186–204.

factors which make for success and cannot possibly include all of them. The value of r in such a situation tells us to what extent the test has measured the real determinants of success, and hence it tells us just how far our prediction ought to follow the test score. When $r = .6$, for example, the best prediction is one which "follows the score" only six-tenths of the way (in standard units); otherwise we are brushing aside as nonexistent all of the determinants which we failed to measure in the test. For the individual who scores 1 standard deviation below the mean on such a test (that is, above 16 per cent of the group), the best guess for future performance is a standing six-tenths of a standard deviation below the mean (that is, better than about 27 per cent of the group). Guidance teachers who have inadequate training in statistics often overlook this fact.

A very useful way to think of correlation is in terms of the partitioning of variance. The total variance of individual scores may be divided into one portion which measures the strength of whatever functional relationship exists between the two variables and another which measures the strength of all other influences. The first portion consists of the variance among the regressed scores, and the second is the remaining variance of individual scores within columns (or rows). You can visualize this in terms of the obviously reduced range of scores within each column compared to the total range on the test. This is a necessary consequence of the fact that as the relationship grows stronger, the ellipse which circumscribes the scores becomes narrower. At the same time, obviously, the range of regressed scores grows wider. What we call the coefficient of correlation is the ratio of the range of regressed scores to the total range of individual scores. Also, r^2 is the ratio of the variance of regressed scores to the total variance. In other words, r^2 tells us what proportion of the variance of individual scores on both measures is common variance, shared by both variables.

Much of what we have said in this chapter should remind you of the differentiation ratio, eta square, which is based on a similar partitioning of variance. In fact, the usual name for eta—that is, the square root of the differentiation ratio—is the correlation ratio. The only difference between eta^2 and r^2 is that the latter is based on an assumption that the functional relationship is consistent throughout the full range of scores, while the former makes no such assumption. The simplest way to judge whether the assumption is appropriate is to make up a chart like Table 15-1 and see if the scores have an elliptical pattern. If not, at least one of the regression lines will be curved rather than straight. There are always two values of eta^2, because in such a case the statistical dependence between the variables is not strictly reciprocal. For example, you can guess a person's vocabulary from his age better than you can guess his age from his vocabulary, because vocabulary grows much more rapidly in childhood than later. Therefore the differentiation ratio based on vocabulary scores, classified by age groups, is greater than that for age scores, classified by vocabulary scores. When the assumption of straight-line regression is justified, r^2 is the correct measure of common variance; when it is not, it will underestimate, just as eta^2 overestimates.

We should like to mention one more of the many uses of correlation in research. It can be used to estimate the strength of an extraneous influence which cannot be controlled in an experiment or in a series of observations and which influences the results in a systematic rather than a random manner. For example, observations such as those in Table 15-1 will tend to slightly overstate the relationship between father and son, for the following reason: tall men tend to marry tall women, and tall women tend to have tall sons. It would be possible, but very difficult, to eliminate this effect by making sure that in each class of fathers, cases with tall wives were balanced by cases with short wives. In order to do this, we would have to discard many observations which could not be properly matched. However, the effect of the wives can be eliminated if correlation coefficients are calculated between sons and mothers and between husbands and wives, as well as between fathers and sons. When an influence has been eliminated in this manner, we say that it has been "partialed out," or held constant statistically, and we refer to the revised figure for correlation between fathers and sons as a partial correlation.

The technique of partial correlation makes it possible to investigate many complex social and biological phenomena in which it is impossible experimentally to isolate different causal factors which all contribute to the final result. Theoretically the method can be used to "partial out" the effects of a number of extraneous influences simultaneously, but this is rarely practical, because of the amount of chance error which accumulates in such situations. Another way of doing this, called factor analysis, will be discussed in Chapter 16.

Chapter 16

NEW STRATEGIES
FOR SCIENCE

•

THE SCIENTIFIC ERA is reckoned from the middle of the seventeenth century. From that time to the present, according to a recent estimate, the fund of human knowledge has doubled about once in every 15 years.* This is a rate of growth which is equivalent to that of money which is drawing 4.75 per cent interest annually, and it means that today we know about two million times as much about the universe we live in and the creatures which inhabit it as was known shortly after the death of Galileo. In the next fifteen years, scientists will learn as much more as in all previous history. Does this seem incredible? Almost any active scientific worker, struggling to keep abreast of the flood of new developments, will quite readily agree that in his own special field twice as much is known now as was known in 1950, four times as much as in 1935, and that the present pace of development is more rapid than ever before.

This knowledge explosion has many fairly obvious reasons, including the increased number of scientists, better instru-

* Derek J. Price, *Little Science, Big Science* (New York: Columbia University Press, 1963).

ments, and faster exchange of knowledge. One important reason which is not so obvious is the improvement in what we now call the design of experiments. Francis Bacon (1561–1626), the prophet of the new era, argued very eloquently that men should trust experiment rather than deductive reasoning, because, as he put it, the subtlety of nature is far greater than that of our own minds, but he himself did not know how to conduct an experiment in the modern sense of the word. This is a skill which scientists have improved bit by bit. Like every other aspect of scientific work, it has undergone the most rapid development in the most recent period. Today, in many fields of science, graduate students are expected to take a course in the design of experiments, after completing an advanced course in statistical methods. And just as in other worthwhile courses, they meet up with new ideas which make it necessary to discard some old ideas.

Until about thirty years ago, nobody questioned that the correct way to perform scientific research was to isolate the action of one influence at a time, in order to study it in its purest form, without interference. The definition of an ideal scientific experiment was that impossible situation in which one condition was varied at will by the experimenter, while all other conditions remained constant. If it were ever possible to achieve this situation, the results would speak for themselves, and statistical analysis would be superfluous, like gilding the lily. Increasingly, scientists have relied on statistical methods to measure the effect of extraneous influences, and thus to achieve control in their analysis over variables which they were not able to control experimentally. However, the basic objective remained the same: to cause one influence, which is called the experimental variable, to vary systematically and to hold all other influences constant while measuring changes in the dependent variable. This supposed need to study the effects of only one influence at a time has been largely responsible for the skepticism which has often been expressed about the possibility of coming to grips with complex social and psychological problems by quantitative methods.

The progress of statistical theory has changed this situation. The new strategy of science is to complicate experiments rather than to simplify them, by systematically varying several kinds of experimental treatment at the same time. The man most responsible for this change was R. A. Fisher, whose book, *The Design of Experiments,** is a landmark in the history of scientific method.

FACTORIAL DESIGN

Fisher illustrated one aspect of modern experimental design with the following fictitious situation:

> Sixteen passengers on a liner discover that they are an exceptionally representative body. Four are Englishmen, four are Scots, four are Irish, and four are Welsh. There are also four each of four different ages, 35, 45, 55, and 65, and no two of the same age are of the same nationality. By profession also four are lawyers, four soldiers, four doctors and four clergymen, and no two of the same profession are of the same age or of the same nationality.
>
> It appears, also, that four are bachelors, four married, four widowed and four divorced, and that no two of the same marital status are of the same profession, or the same age, or the same nationality. Finally, four are conservatives, four liberals, four socialists and four fascists, and no two of the same political sympathies are of the same marital status, or the same profession, or the same age, or the same nationality.

If you are a puzzle enthusiast, you should have some fun reconstructing this situation. (Do not give up too soon, for it is quite possible.) However, let us suppose that you too are a passenger on this liner, and you would like to spend

---

* Ronald A. Fisher, *The Design of Experiments* (Edinburgh: Oliver & Boyd, 1935).

your time on the voyage in a way which is profitable to science. You decide to investigate the effect of whiskey on verbal fluency. The general procedure for your experiment will be to bring each passenger, sober, to the ship's bar, administer a short test of verbal fluency (for example, instruct him to say as many words as he can in one minute, using a first word that starts with *a*, a second word that starts with *b*, and so forth); follow this with two ounces of whiskey, and repeat the test (starting at a later point in the alphabet) after five minutes. His score is the difference in words-spoken-per-minute before and after imbibing the whiskey. Now, if you can enlist for the experiment either the representative group described by Fisher, who are seated at one end of the ship's salon, or sixteen unmarried conservative Irish traveling salesmen, all aged thirty-five, seated at the other end, which group would you prefer to use as subjects in your experiment?

It should be clear that the result obtained with the heterogeneous group, as opposed to the homogeneous group, will be a more useful guide for future experience in dealing with people generally. But besides, you have a chance to discover whether whiskey affects doctors in the same way as clergymen, or married men in the same way as bachelors. Indeed, it will be possible to consider the results by profession, by age, by marital status, by nationality, or by political sympathy, and no matter which of these comparisons you make, the groups you compare will be balanced in the four remaining respects. Furthermore, you will have an opportunity to discover whether differences which exist between older soldiers and clergymen also exist between younger soldiers and clergymen, or whether socialist lawyers resemble socialist soldiers any more than fascist lawyers resemble fascist soldiers.

There are even more complicated quetions on which your data will have bearing, such as whether the differences among the professions depend in part on their marital status at some ages, but not at other ages. In short, in addition to obtaining evidence on how the individuals differ in their response to whiskey according to their status in any one of five different schemes of classification, you will also learn whether there is *interaction* among those schemes. After all, marriage must mean something different to a clergyman and a doctor, and political sympathy must mean something different to a lawyer and a soldier.

Of course, if you want reasonably reliable answers to all these questions, it will be necessary to examine more than sixteen subjects. The experiment should be *replicated,* that is, the same basic design should be repeated with several blocks of sixteen subjects each. If in one block the thirty-five-year-old doctor is an unmarried socialist Scot, in another he might be a widowed conservative Welshman. All the same comparisons are possible within each replication, and their effects can be summed overall, to make the conclusions more reliable. Also, in different blocks fluency lists can start with different letters, to study the influence of this variable.

The following are some readily understandable realistic instances of interaction which have appeared in factorial experiments: (1) the effectiveness of a given amount of nitrate fertilizer depends on the amount of phosphate which is used along with it; (2) the efficiency with which an easy task is performed, under time pressure, is increased by inducing a relatively high level of anxiety in the subjects, but the same level of anxiety will disrupt the performance of a more complex task; (3) the tendency of male rats to exhibit maternal behavior after administration of certain female hormones depends on the nature of their social experience as infants, as well as on the intactness of a certain small portion of the brain.

In order to make use of such complex factorial designs for research, two conditions must be satisfied: (1) We must be able to partition the sum of squares in a way that allocates a proper proportion of the total to each source of score variation. The task here is in principle no different from the analysis we have already made into a between-sum and a within-sum, and although more complicated formulas are needed, they serve only, as Fisher puts it, to provide a convenient arrangement of arithmetic for the purpose. (2) We must have some means to determine whether a given sum of squares, which is related to a particular source, exceeds the value that it might be expected to have by chance, under the null hypothesis. This is a more difficult matter, and by its solution Fisher gained a kind of immortality which comes to few men. The table of F—so designated by an American statistician, George W. Snedecor, who constructed it to facilitate the use of Fisher's method—is used in all tests of significance based on analysis of variance.

F stands for the ratio between two mean squares, each of which is an independent estimate of the mean square in the same universe. How great this ratio may be by chance—that is, say, 95 times in 100, or 99 times in 100, or 999 times in 1000—depends on the amount of information which is available for forming *each* of the estimates. Therefore F is a three-dimensional function, and the condensed table of its critical values occupies several pages. Within this table, the critical values which correspond to the chi-square distributions occupy one row, those related to Student's distribution (see Appendix E) occupy one column, and those related to the table of normal probability occupy one cell, at the intersection of that row and column. Most of the table permits us to make exact tests which those distributions do not permit, using more than two groups at a time, and taking the size of the groups into account. In other words, the *F-ratio* (or *variance ratio*) is a master concept which governs many kinds of probability. It is a unifying principle which underlies all statistical methods.

FACTOR ANALYSIS

The factorial design of experiments presupposes that we know the essential factors in the problem we are investigating and that they are subject to our control. This condition is often met not only in laboratory research, but also in the analysis of survey data or observations in the field. However, it is sometimes the case, especially in exploring relatively new areas of research, that the essential factors are still to be identified. For this purpose, there is a special type of experimental design called *factor analysis,* which utilizes the correlations among many variables.

You will readily recall that the existence of a correlation between two measures tells us nothing directly about the nature of the causal connection between them. However, when we study intercorrelations among a great many variables, we can sometimes draw conclusions about the distribution of causal factors. For example, if a personality test includes half a dozen items which tend to be answered in the same way by the same persons and half a dozen other items which also tend to agree among themselves but not with items of the first group, then we have no hesitation in asserting that this test is measuring two different things. This kind of "cluster analysis" is an elementary form of factor analysis. In a more highly developed form, factor analysis depends on matrix algebra to tell us how many dimensions, or descriptive categories, are needed in order to explain all of the observed intercorrelation of a set of measures.

There is a convenient geometric way to represent factor analysis, but it requires that we use a "cosine model" of correlation instead of the "slope model" which we used in the previous chapter. When correlation is represented by the slope of a regression line, it always requires exactly n dimensions to deal with the relationships among n variables. We shall see that this is not true in the cosine model.

In a right triangle, the cosine of either acute angle is the ratio of the length of the adjacent side to the hypotenuse. If two lines intersect, the projection on one line of a unit length on the other line is equal to the cosine. Let us think of each scale of measurement as a straight line with a positive and a negative direction, and with a zero point which coincides with the zero point of all other scales. In Figure 7, four scales are shown, including the negative extension of only one of these, *D*. The broken lines are perpendiculars which mark off the projections of *A* on the other scales. Variable *A* has a high positive correlation with *B*, a moderate positive correlation with *C*, and a low negative correlation with *D*. Similar perpendiculars to *A*, from *B*, *C*, and *D*, will show that each of these relationships is reciprocal. By this method, *r* has a limiting value of $+1$, which it approaches when two scales exactly coincide and agree in direction. If they coincide, but have opposite direction, $r = -1$. When the scales are at right angles to each other, $r = 0$.

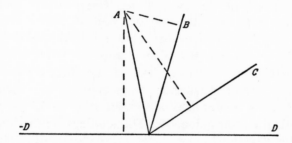

FIGURE 7. The representation of correlations in the cosine model. The projection onto any scale of a unit length on another scale equals *r*, their correlation.

Figure 7 demonstrates that it is possible for four variables, or more, to be so related that their correlations can be represented in only two dimensions. Suppose that correlations have been measured among a dozen variables. It is conceivable, though unlikely, that all these correlations can be represented in two dimensions, that is, by drawing a dozen lines radiating from one point on a plane surface, and all at the proper angles so that the projection of a unit length along one line, on any other, is equal to the correlation coefficient between those two measures. If this is not possible, it may still be possible to construct a model with all the proper angles in three dimensions, either by pushing dowel sticks into a ball of clay, or by plotting the ends of the scales on the surface of a sphere. When more than three dimensions are required, one must use matrix algebra to handle the problem efficiently. However, if we were to find that a set of correlations among many variables can be modeled, geometrically, in only two or three dimensions, we would have good reason to assume that only two or three causal factors are responsible for all of the common variance among the measures.

The first part of a factor analysis consists of an algebraic solution to the question of how many dimensions are needed to represent all of the correlations. When all the correlation coefficients among n measures are known, there is a certain amount of redundancy, or duplication of information, because some of the correlations place limits on the values which other correlations can have. All of the information can be restated in a smaller number of correlations, called *loadings,* between the n scales and a smaller number of factors, or hypothetical causal influences. The loadings on the hypothetical factors "explain" the original correlations in the sense that from them it is possible to reconstruct the first set. The necessary number of factors is never greater than the number of variables, n, minus as many of the triangular numbers (1, 3, 6, 10, etc.) as do not exceed n in value. (This rule takes account of some savings in dimensions which are made possible by introducing into the cosine model certain concepts of vector measurement. It will not be necessary to explain those in detail, in order to state the essentials of factor analysis.) Thus, the correlations among 15 measures can surely be reconstructed from their loadings on 10 hypothetical factors, those among 12 measures by loadings on 8 factors, those among 40 measures by loadings on 32 factors. However, in any particular case the analysis of nonchance intercorrelations will very likely show that a still smaller number will suffice to reconstruct the correlations with reasonable accuracy—that is, making some allowance for experimental error. If we find that the correlations among 15 measures can be reconstructed from loadings on only 3 factors, we have good reason to believe that in reality only 3 causal influences are responsible for all of the common variance among these measures. This is an application of what is called the principle of parsimony, or economy, in scientific explanation.

Factor analysis has been developed very largely by psychologists, although it can be applied in other fields. It had its start when Charles Spearman, a British psychologist-statistician, developed an ingenious mathematical device in an attempt to prove his theory that all of the intercorrelation among various tests of mental ability results from the operation of a single general factor, called g, or general intelligence. His formula used only 4 correlations at a time, selected from the 6 correlations among 4 tests. The method was greatly expanded by L. L. Thurstone, an American psychologist, who used it to show that at least 7 "primary mental abilities" must be assumed. Thurstone's method was then used by J. P. Guilford to show that the items used in so-called tests of *introversion* were actually measuring three distinct tendencies in behavior, which he designated as thinking introversion, social introversion, and emotional depression or moodiness.

These were relatively simple applications. In more complex applications, the problem of interpreting the factors can be quite difficult, especially when there are more than three dimensions in the factor space, so that a physical model is not possible. This is the second phase of a factor analysis, and usually this is the more interesting part. Many different sets of reference axes can be used to define positions in the same space. Let us illustrate this with a geographic analogy. Although we locate positions on the globe by reference to the equator and the Greenwich meridian, we could use, if we liked, one great circle through Paris and Montreal, and another through Paris and Rio de Janeiro. Then the position of New York City could be defined as the intersection of a perpendicular which is about 53° West on the Paris-Montreal circle and another which is about 30° South on the Paris-Rio circle. This system would be less convenient than the other, but it is equally exact. The second part of a factor analysis consists in a hunt for the most meaningful directions for the necessary number of reference axes, or factors. It is important to recognize that, just as in our geographic analogy, it is not essential that these axes be at right angles to each other.

If the factor space has only two dimensions, everything can be plotted on a sheet of paper. With three dimensions the task is more difficult, but we can still approach it with ordinary perceptual habits, perhaps by building a model and turning it in our hands, looking for three "points of view" from which the entire constellation can be seen most clearly. This task of rotating the system through its various dimensions in order to select the best positions for the reference axes need not be a purely subjective matter. It is possible to set up mathematical criteria for meaningful axes, which are analogous to the least-squares criterion which is used in fitting a curve to a set of points. When that is done, the computational work can be turned over to a computer. A few years ago a man might have spent months in finding a questionable solution to the rotation of axes for a relatively small problem, but today computers do a better job, for much larger problems, in a matter of minutes.

Charles E. Osgood and his associates have used factor analysis in their research on the nature of meaning in human thought and speech. Most words have connotations as well as denotations. For example, the words "girl," "gal," and "maiden" can be used to denote the same object, but with different connotations. Osgood's subjects are required to say whether particular words, like these, seem to them more straight or curved, more soft or hard, more quick or slow, and so forth. Some of these judgments, perhaps most of them, may seem nonsensical, but the fact that they are not is demonstrated by agreement among the judgments by different subjects. However, the most interesting correlations are not those which measure agreement among the subjects, but those which measure the alikeness of the concepts being judged. Factor analyses of these correlations reveal that all over the world, people of all classes speaking many different languages have their thoughts shaped in large part by the same three dimensions of connotative meaning: *evaluation* (good versus bad), *power* (strong versus weak), and *activity* (fast versus slow). The similarity of results in different cultures is a surprising revelation of the importance of fundamental biological orientations in determining our thinking processes. However, the relative importance of these three factors may change from one individual to the next, and differences in personality can show up as different connotations given to the same word.

In one study, a young woman suffering from a classical split personality of the Dr. Jekyll and Mr. Hyde type judged the same concepts twice, in her two different states. Her two personalities, "Eve White" and "Eve Black," attached very different connotations to such words as *love, child,* and *sin.* In another study, it was shown that the attitudes of college students toward thirteen ideal "ways of life" were determined by four factors, which the authors designated as Dynamism, Socialization, Control, and Venturousness. For example, one way of life which might be summed up as "group action toward common goals" became, in factor terms, a "socialized venturous dynamism," while another, which might be summed up as "wholesome enjoyment of simple comforts," became "passive socialization" in the factor analysis.*

* Charles E. Osgood has written a book, with George J. Suci and Percy H. Tannenbaum, called *The Measurement of Meaning* (Urbana: University of Illinois Press, 1957).

MORE COMPUTER MAGIC

We shall end with an example of statistical analysis which will
not be concerned with complexity of experimental design, but
will show how the most elementary of all statistical procedures,
averaging, can acquire new power when it is aided by the

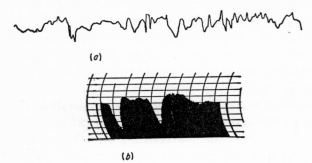

(a)

(b)

FIGURE 8. (a) Sample of simultaneous EEG record
of voltage changes on the surface of visual cortex of
a cat's brain following bright flash of light. (b) Aver-
age of fifty such individual records. *Source:* Mary
Brazier, "Studies of Evoked Responses by Flash in
Man and Cat," in *Reticular Formation of the Brain,*
Henry Ford Hospital International Symposium (New
York: Little, Brown & Co., 1958).

great speed of electronic devices. The wavy line in Figure
8 (a) is a record of tiny voltage changes on the surface of one
portion of a cat's brain, for about one-fifth of a second
following a bright flash of light. The record is from the visual
cortex and was made under moderate pentobarbital anes-
thesia. Such recordings are difficult to analyze, because the
brain is continuously active, responding to many internal as
well as external stimulations. Figure 8 (b) shows what happens when fifty such individual records, all made under the
same conditions, are averaged by an electronic computer
which is instructed to remember and then total the recorded
voltages at intervals of one-thousandth of a second.

In this averaged record the responses to other forms of stimulation, as well as the spontaneous activity of the brain itself, are eliminated as "error," and we see clearly that in the same area of the brain there are two different responses to the flash, one following the other by about seven hundredths of a second. This proves that the message goes from the eye to this portion of the brain by two different paths. (The slower path is not necessarily longer, but it must involve more transfer points or synapses between separate nerve cells, because at these points the nerve impulse is delayed slightly.) Mary Brazier found this second response to the flash at some parts of the brain but not at other parts, and she also showed that the units involved in the first and second responses were influenced by various drugs in different ways.

Thus we have returned to our point of departure: that even with the finest instrumentation and the most careful procedures, there is no experiment without error, and hence no science possible which does not recognize error as an inevitable part of its data. When we say, "error is inevitable," this is just another way of saying, "the world is complicated." The business of science is to make this complicated world seem as simple as possible, simple enough for our mental grasp, and in performing this task it finds statistics indispensable. Astronomers, economists, physicists, physiologists, psychologists— scientific workers of every discipline—all rely on the same basic principles of probability to test the validity of their hypotheses. The accelerated flow of scientific knowledge in the present day is in no small part due to the development of more powerful statistical methods—a process which is now going on with the same explosive speed that characterizes all scientific advance. The experiences in field and laboratory of the scientist add up to knowledge more quickly, more surely, because of formulas which had their beginning in exasperation at the seemingly capricious behavior of those rolling bones.

Appendixes

APPENDIX A

THE ZERO SUM OF DEVIATIONS

First, define a deviation as the difference between an individual score and the mean:

$$x_i = X_i - \overline{X}.$$

The sum of all the deviation scores in a distribution is equal to the sum of the separate terms of the definition equation. That is,

$$\Sigma x_i = \Sigma X_i - n\overline{X}.$$

Notice that the summation sign is used to indicate the sum of all the deviation scores, and of all the raw scores, because these are changing quantities, but the sum of a constant, taken n times, is indicated as a product.

Observe, however, that this product, $n\overline{X}$, equals

$$n\,(\Sigma X_i)/n = \Sigma X_i.$$

Therefore, substituting in the previous equation,

$$\Sigma x_i = \Sigma X_i - \Sigma X_i = 0.$$

APPENDIX B

THE MINIMAL SUM OF SQUARES

Each deviation is the difference between an individual score and the mean of its distribution:

$$x_i = X_i - \overline{X}.$$

Therefore a squared deviation score equals

$$X_i^2 - 2X_i\overline{X} + \overline{X}^2.$$

The sum of squared deviations for n scores is obtained by summing these three terms separately, thus:

$$\Sigma X_i^2 - 2\Sigma X_i\overline{X} + n\overline{X}^2.$$

Again, as in the previous proof, we have written the sum of a constant, taken n times, as a product.

Wherever $\overline{X}$ appears, we may substitute $\Sigma X_i/n$. This gives

$$\Sigma X_i^2 - 2\Sigma X_i \, (\Sigma X_i/n) + n \, (\Sigma X_i/n)^2.$$

Simplifying, this becomes

$$\Sigma X_i^2 - 2 \, (\Sigma X_i)^2/n + (\Sigma X_i)^2/n.$$

Combining like terms, we obtain one of the most important computational formulas in all statistical work:

$$\Sigma x_i^2 = \Sigma X_i^2 - (\Sigma X_i)^2/n.$$

Now we wish to show that no smaller sum of squared deviation scores can be obtained by taking the deviations from any point other than the mean. We therefore define a trial deviation, d_i, as the difference between an individual score and some other point, $\overline{X} + A$, where A can have any value whatever. That is,

$$d_i = X_i - (\overline{X} + A).$$

We repeat all the same steps taken above. The value of a squared trial deviation, so defined, equals

$$X_i^2 + \overline{X}^2 - 2X_i\overline{X} + A^2 - 2X_iA + 2A\overline{X}.$$

Summing each term separately, this becomes

$$\Sigma X_i^2 + n\overline{X}^2 - 2\Sigma X_i\overline{X} + nA^2 - 2\Sigma X_iA + 2nA\overline{X}.$$

Wherever $\overline{X}$ appears, substitute $(\Sigma X_i/n)$.

$$\Sigma X_i^2 + n(\Sigma X_i/n)^2 - 2\Sigma X_i(\Sigma X_i/n)$$
$$+ nA^2 - 2\Sigma_i XA + 2nA(\Sigma X_i/n).$$

Simplifying within terms, and combining like terms, we finally obtain:

$$\Sigma d_i^2 = \Sigma X_i^2 - (\Sigma X_i)^2/n + nA^2.$$

The first two terms on the right, by themselves, are equal to the sum of squares from the mean, as developed in the first part of this proof. The final term is an extra. It is what is added to the sum of squares by shifting the point of reference from $\overline{X}$ to $\overline{X} + A$. This result will play a key part in the proof of the variance law, and reference to it will be made at several times when we discuss the partitioning of a sum of squares.

APPENDIX C

THE VARIANCE LAW

Let X be one distribution and Y another. Let U be the universe in which each member is a sum of one member of X and one member of Y.

If there are m members of X, and n members of Y, then U contains mn members. To obtain these sums, each X_i is used n times (once with each Y_i), and each Y_i is used m times (once with each X_i). Therefore

$$\Sigma U_i = m\Sigma Y_i + n\Sigma X_i$$

and $$\overline{U} = (m\Sigma Y_i + n\Sigma X_i) \ / \ mn = \overline{X} + \overline{Y}.$$

The universe U may be considered as made up of m subsets, each of which was constructed by adding one member of X, X_i, to each member of Y in turn. Each of these subsets has n members. To find the sum of squares for the universe, Σu_i^2, we shall first consider the contribution which a single subset makes to that sum.

This contribution can be analyzed into two parts:
(1) a sum of squared deviations from the subset mean, and
(2) the squared difference between universe mean and subset mean, times the number in the subset. (This second portion is equivalent to the nA^2 of the final equation in Appendix B.)

Since the subset is formed by adding a constant to each member of Y in turn, it has a "within sum" which is equal to Σy_i^2. This is because adding a constant to each score in a distribution does not change the scatter of the scores, but only shifts them without disturbing their relative positions. For all

m subsets, the total contribution to the universe sum of squares, from this source, equals $m\Sigma y_i^2$.

We turn our attention to the second component. The squared difference between the subset mean and the universe mean is

$$[(X_i + \overline{Y}) - (\overline{X} + \overline{Y})]^2 = (X_i - \overline{X})^2 = x_i^2.$$

This is true for each of the m subsets, but in each case the value of x_i is different. Since there are n members in each subset, the total contribution from this source equals $n\Sigma x_i^2$.

Taking both sources together,

$$\Sigma u^2 = m\Sigma y_i^2 + n\Sigma x_i^2.$$

To find the mean square, we must divide by mn, the number of members in the universe. Hence,

$$\sigma_U^2 = \frac{m\Sigma y_i^2 + n\Sigma x_i^2}{mn} = \frac{\Sigma y_i^2}{n} + \frac{\Sigma x_i^2}{m} = \sigma_Y^2 + \sigma_X^2.$$

The same argument can be repeated, for a universe composed of sums of elements taken from more than two distributions. Therefore,

$$(\sigma_{A+B+\ldots K})^2 = \sigma_A^2 + \sigma_B^2 + \ldots + \sigma_K^2.$$

This equation can be expressed as follows: *the variance of a universe of sums is equal to the sum of the variances of the parent populations.*

APPENDIX D

VARIANCE OF BINOMIAL AND POISSON DISTRIBUTIONS

(In the following discussion, we must remember the distinction between N, the number of opportunities for an event to occur, and n, the number of scores in a distribution.)

By definition, σ^2, called variance, equals $\Sigma x_i^2/n$.

In a binomial distribution with $N = 1$, a representative sample of n scores includes np scores of 1, and $n(1 - p)$ scores of 0. The mean score of the distribution equals p. Therefore the sum of squared deviations equals

$$\Sigma x_i^2 = np\,(1 - p)^2 + n\,(1 - p)\,(-p)^2$$
$$= np\,(1 - 2p + p^2) + (n - np)\,p^2$$
$$= np - 2np^2 + np^3 + np^2 - np^3$$
$$= np - np^2 = np\,(1 - p) = npq.$$

To find variance, this sum of squares must be divided by n, the number of scores. Hence the variance of such a distribution equals pq.

Any binomial distribution with N greater than 1 can be regarded as a universe formed by taking samples of size N from the distribution for $N = 1$. Therefore, by the Variance Law (see Appendix C), the variance of any such distribution equals Npq.

In a Poisson distribution, p approaches 0 as a limit, and therefore q approaches 1 as a limit. Consequently Npq equals Np, and accordingly the variance of a Poisson distribution is equal to its mean.

APPENDIX E

SMALL SAMPLES

The discussion of confidence intervals in Chapter 11 and of the difference between sample means in Chapter 12 does not take account of the refinements needed when working with small samples. The development of exact tests based on small samples is of great practical importance, because each year such tests save many thousands of scientist-hours, by making small samples do the work for which large samples would otherwise be required. Here we shall merely indicate the general nature of the adjustment required by the most important of these methods, which makes use of *Student's distribution*. (The "student" in this case was W. S. Gossett, who worked for the Guinness breweries, which had a company rule against the publication of research by employees. The rule was relaxed just enough to permit him to publish his epoch-making discovery, in 1908, in this modest anonymity.)

If, for each score in a random sample, we could know its deviation from the population mean, the resulting mean square would be an unbiased estimate of the population mean square. But we do not know the population mean, and therefore we take deviations from the sample mean. The sum of squares is therefore too small by an amount which is equal to n times the squared difference between the sample mean and the unknown population mean. It is possible to adjust for this discrepancy by using $n - 1$, rather than n, as a divisor. The result is an unbiased estimate of population variance, that is, one which tends over the long run to average out to the correct value. However, although this series of estimates is unbiased, it is also unbalanced, for it includes more estimates that are too low than those that are too high. This means too many low estimates of standard errors, and too many high values for the ratios which use them in the denominator. Too many, that is, if critical values for the ratios are taken from the normal table of probability. A new probability table is needed, and this is *Student's distribution,* commonly called *t.*

The table of *t* has different critical values according to the size of the sample, or samples, in the particular case. For example, the 5 per cent critical values, to establish a confidence interval for the mean of a sample of fifteen cases, would be 2.145 instead of 1.960, the value in the normal distribution; for a sample of thirty cases, it would be 2.045.

Under some circumstances—particularly when sampling is not from a near-normal population—other small sample methods are more appropriate. These are usually designated as "nonparametric" or "distribution-free" statistics, meaning that they make no mathematical assumptions about the form of distribution in the original population. The exact test for independence, described in Chapter 5, is one such method.

APPENDIX F

THE BEST-FIT REGRESSION LINE

For simplicity, we assume in this discussion that all scores are standardized.

Let x_i and y_i be paired scores, and let rx_i be called a regressed score, which we symbolize y'_i.

We want to learn what value of r will give regressed scores such that the mean squared discrepancy (i.e., error of prediction) between regressed scores and actual scores has the smallest possible value.

Since, by definition, $y'_i = rx_i$, we may write

$$y_i - y'_i = y_i - rx_i$$

Squaring, $$(y_i - y'_i)^2 = y_i^2 - 2rx_iy_i + r^2x_i^2$$

Summing, $$\Sigma(y_i - y'_i)^2 = \Sigma y_i^2 - 2r\Sigma(x_iy_i) + r^2\Sigma x_i^2$$

Dividing by n,
$$\frac{\Sigma(y_i - y'_i)^2}{n} = \frac{\Sigma y_i^2}{n} - \frac{2r\Sigma(x_iy_i)}{n} + \frac{r^2\Sigma x_i^2}{n}.$$

In place of r, we shall substitute $\Sigma(x_iy_i)/n$, that is, the mean product of paired standardized scores. This gives:

$$\frac{\Sigma(y_i - y'_i)^2}{n} = \frac{\Sigma y_i^2}{n} - 2\frac{\Sigma(x_iy_i)}{n} \cdot \frac{\Sigma(x_iy_i)}{n} + \left[\frac{\Sigma(x_iy_i)}{n}\right]^2 \frac{\Sigma x_i^2}{n}.$$

Since we are dealing with standard scores, $\Sigma x_i^2/n = \Sigma y_i^2/n = 1$. Taking advantage of this, and combining like terms,

$$\frac{\Sigma(y_i - y'_i)^2}{n} = 1 - \left[\frac{\Sigma(x_iy_i)}{n}\right]^2.$$

To test whether any other value of r can give a smaller sum of squared discrepancies, we write a trial value of r, thus:

$$r = \frac{\Sigma(x_iy_i)}{n} \pm A.$$

where A can have any value whatever. If we substitute this value of r, instead of the other, the end result would be

$$\frac{\Sigma(y_i - y'_i)^2}{n} = 1 - \left[\frac{\Sigma(x_iy_i)}{n}\right]^2 + A^2.$$

Hence, we conclude that the smallest mean squared discrepancy results when r is the mean product of paired scores. Using that value, by further simplifying the earlier result, we can also write

$$\frac{\Sigma(y_i - y'_i)^2}{n} = 1 - r^2.$$

That is, r^2 is the proportion of explained variance, and $1 - r^2$, the remainder, is the proportion of error variance.

NAME INDEX

Allen, E. J., 152

Bartlett, M. S., 27
Bayes, Thomas, 16
Bental, E., 64, 144
Berkeley, George, 17
Bernoulli, James, 29
Bihari, B., 64, 144
Borkiewicz, L., 5
Bravais, A., 158
Brazier, Mary A. B., 176 f.
Brown, Robert, 84

Cauchy, Augustin Louis, 133
Chang, Shueh-Shen, 45
Coleman, B., 129

Darwin, Charles, 154
David, F. N., 8

Eccles, J. C., 11
Einstein, Albert, 85
Evarts, E. V., 64, 144

Fermat, Pierre de, 22
Findikyan, N., 97
Fisher, Ronald A., 46, 166–169
Frei, J. V., 78

Galilei, Galileo, 13 f., 35
Galton, Francis, 154 f., 158
Geiger, Hans, 77
Geissler, Heinrich, 139
Glaviano, V. V., 129
Gossett, W. S., 184
Guilford, J. P., 173

Halley, Edmund, 49
Hargenvillier, 60
Heisenberg, Werner, 10 f.
Huttenlocher, P. R., 64, 144

Jacobson, A. L., 88 f.

Kalmus, H., 62
Kapteyn, Jacobus C., 7
Kepler, Johannes, 52
Kimble, D., 88 f.

Laplace, Pierre Simon de, 7, 12, 31
Lashley, K. S., 89
Lavender, J. P., 45
Lee, A., 156
Leucippus, 10

McConnell, J. V., 88 f.
Marsh, J. T., 45
Morgan, Thomas Hunt, 43

Osgood, Charles E., 174 f.

Pascal, Blaise, 21 f., 132
Pearson, Karl, 25, 136, 154–156, 158
Plair, C. M., 149
Poisson, Siméon Denis, 5, 76 f., 133
Pomerantz, Martin, 4
Price, D. J. de S., 164
Przibram, Karl, 85

Quetelet, Lambert, 54–57, 60, 133, 157

Rasmussen, A. P., 45
Reynolds, E. L., 160
Ritchie, A. C., 78
Rutherford, Ernest, 77

Sells, S. B., 97
Selye, Hans, 44
Snedecor, George W., 169
Spearman, Charles, 173
Sturkie, P. D., 128
Suci, George J., 175

Tachi, Minoru, 160
Tannenbaum, Percy H., 175
Thurstone, Louis L., 173

Vogel, J. A., 128

Waugh, W. O'N., 78
Wilens, S. L., 149

Yerkes, Robert M., 57, 87

SUBJECT INDEX

absolute deviations, 82, 90
analysis of variance, 169
aptitude tests, 160 f.
arithmetic mean, *see* mean
arrangements, 14, 16 f.
average deviation, 82 f.
average man, 56 f.

bar diagram, 100
best-fit line, 157, 185–187
between-groups sum, 93; and systematic influences, 92
bimodal, 61
binomial coefficients, 37
binomial distribution, 37, 66; discreteness of, 100; mean of, 51 f.; mean square of, 83; standard deviation of, 108, 183; test of fit, 134; use in genetics, 41 f., 132
binomial probability, 36
Brownian movement, 84–86

Cauchy distribution, 133
chance, 13 f.; empirical estimate of, 94 f.
chi-square, 135; distribution, 136–138; table described, 138; tests of fit by, 139–141; test of independence by, 142–150
cluster analysis, 170
combinations, 17, 19–21; formula for, 21

compound events, 31–33; probability of, 41
computer use, 176
conditional probability, 40, 42
confidence interval, 120–122; how broadened, 122 f.
confidence levels, 110 f., 128
contingency table, 147
continuous distributions, 102
correlation, product-moment, 158–163; cosine model of, 170–172; formula, 158; partial, 163
correlation ratio, 162

degrees of freedom, 136 f., 147
dependent events, 40
design of experiments, 165–169
deviation scores, 53; zero sum of, 178
dice, and laws of chance, 8 f., 13 f., 48
differentiation ratio, 93, 95; and correlation, 162; without bias, 98
dimensionality, 172
discontinuous distributions, 101
distribution-free statistics, 185

e, 26, 72–75
equally possible cases, 12 f., 35, 37

error, experimental, 1, 177; versus design, 4; versus information, 3; law of, 79, 112; versus mistakes, 2; systematic, 6
error ratio, 93
error sum, 91
error variance, 187
exact test, 45 f., 185; formula for, 46
expected frequencies, 29, 135, 144 f.
expected value, 29 f., 48–53
experimental error, *see* error
explained variance, 187

factor analysis, 169–175
factorial design, 168 f.
factorial number, 18
factor loadings, 172
factor rotation, 173 f.
favorable cases, 22 f.
Fisher's exact test, 45 f.
fit, *see* tests of fit
fourfold table, 143, 147
functional relationship, 2, 98; and correlation, 152

Gaussian curve, 79
geometric distribution, 67–69
good fit, 132; *see also* tests of fit

independence, test of, 142
independence hypothesis, 44 f.
independent, defined, 33, 40
indeterminacy principle, 10
index of discrepancy, 135
insurance, 49 f.
intelligence, distribution of, 111

interaction, 118, 168
inverse probability, 15 f.

joint probability, 33

large numbers, law of, 29 f.
law of error, 79, 112

mean, 50, 176 f.; of binomial distribution, 51 f.; as center of gravity, 54
mean square, *see* variance
median, 62–64
mode, 59, 62
Monte Carlo method, 27
moral statistics, 56
multiplication law, 33, 75

negative binomial distribution, 69–71
nonparametric statistics, 185
normal distribution, 79, 133; described, 104 f.; and grades, 103; as law of error, 112; rule of, 105, 107; tests of fit to, 141; uses of table, 109–111
normal probability integration, 109
null hypothesis, 125, 143, 169

p and *P*, defined, 32
parsimony, principle of, 173
partial correlation, 163
Pascal triangle, 21 f., 25 f., 31 f., 37, 105

Poisson distribution, 5, 76–80, 133; mean square, 84; test of fit, 140 f.

prediction of performance, 161

probability, binomial, 36; defined, 11 f.; of compound events, 31 f., 41; conditional, 40, 42; empirical test of, 25 f.; inverse, 15 f.; of zero score, 74

probability density, 136

product-moment correlation, *see* correlation

quality control, 81 f.

random defined, 5

random digits, 26 f., 94

randomness, patterns of, 6

range, 81 f., 90

rectangular distribution, 114 f.

regressed score, 157

regression, 155

regression line, 157, 185–187

representative scores, 52 f., 58

sample universe, *see* universe of samples

sampling experiment, 26

scatter, 81; analysis of, 90

score, v

shrinkage, 73 f.

significance, 23, 128

small samples, 184 f.

squares, *see* sum of squares

standard deviation, 106; of binomial distribution, 108, 183; formula for, 107

standard error of the difference, 127

standard score, 108

statistic, vi

statistical mechanics, 53

Student's distribution, 169, 184 f.

sum of absolute deviations, 82, 90

sum of squares, 83, 169; chance and, 84, 91; minimal value, 92, 179

tests of fit, 133; in binomial distribution, 134; in normal distribution, 141; in Poisson distribution, 140 f.

triangular distribution, 115

types, 61

universe, 12; of differences, 18 f., 126; of samples, 18, 114–116, 134; of sample means, 119 f.

variance, 116; correlation and, 161; of differences, 126; partitioning of, 118

variance law, 117; its proof, 181 f.

variance ratio, 169

within-groups sum of squares, 91